KS3 Science

Homework Book 1

Collins

Ed Walsh
Series Editor
Patricia Miller
Nicholas Paul

William Collins's dream of knowledge for all began with the publication of his first book in 1819. A self-educated mill worker, he not only enriched millions of lives, but also founded a flourishing publishing house. Today, staying true to this spirit, Collins books are packed with inspiration, innovation and practical expertise. They place you at the centre of a world of possibility and give you exactly what you need to explore it.

Collins. Freedom to teach.

Published by Collins
An imprint of HarperCollinsPublishers
77-85 Fulham Palace Road
Hammersmith
London
W6 8JB

Browse the complete Collins catalogue at
www.collinseducation.com

© HarperCollinsPublishers Limited 2008

10 9 8 7 6 5 4 3 2 1

ISBN-13 978-0-00-730603-9

British Library Cataloguing in Publication Data. A Catalogue record for this publication is available from the British Library.

Commissioned by Penny Fowler
Project management by Laura Deacon
Edited by Rosie Parrish and Lynn Watkins
Proof read by Camilla Behrens and Anita Clark
Original concept design by Jordan Publishing Design
Page layout and cover design by eMC Design Ltd, www.emcdesign.org.uk
Illustrations by Jerry Fowler

Production by Leonie Kellman

Printed and bound by Martins the Printers, Berwick-upon-Tweed

Contents

Introduction   4

Organisms, Behaviour and Health
Cells, Tissues and Organs   6
Reproduction   13

Chemical and Material Behaviour
Working in a Laboratory   21
Particles and Reactions   35

Energy, Electricity and Forces
Energy Transfers   46
Forces and Speed   55

The Environment, Earth and Universe
Classification and Food Webs   64
Weathering and Fossils   73

Notes   84
Student progress cards   89
Answers to test yourself questions   91

Introduction

Welcome to Collins KS3 Science!

Exciting homework for every Student Book spread

The Homework Book contains 3 exciting and levelled activities for every spread in the Student Book. There are three styles of question: test yourself, creative and digital so that learning science is engaging and fun.

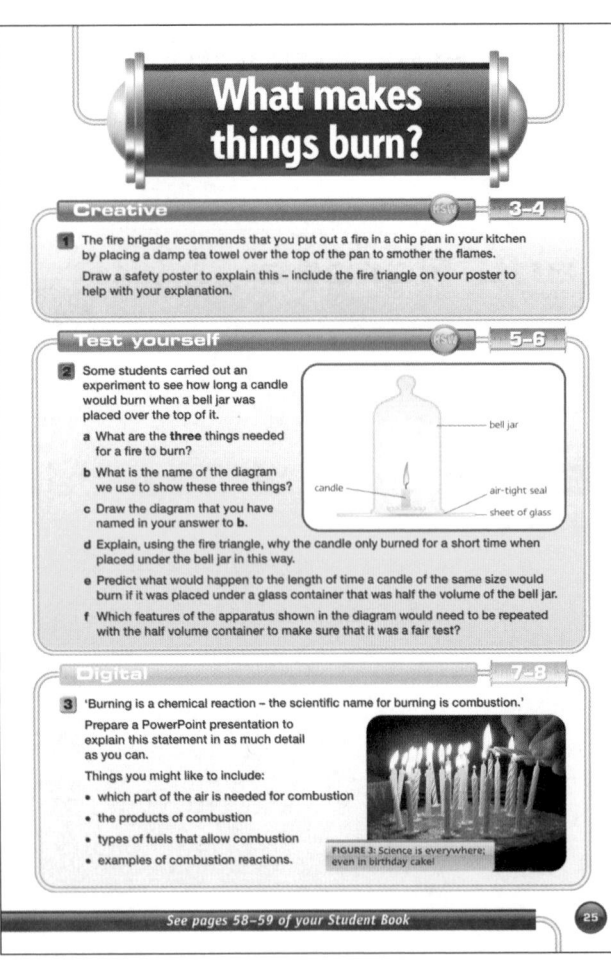

Test yourself

Test your knowledge of a topic with comprehensive test yourself questions. At the back of the book you are able to check your answers or if you don't want to you can tear them out at the start of your course. These questions will give you helpful extra practice and prepare you for school tests to succeed at KS3 and prepare for GCSE.

Creative

Do you want to be a journalist for a day? How about running an advertising campaign? Or how about designing a colourful poster for your classroom?

With creative questions you can really put your science knowledge to the test with a full range of engaging activities making science fun.

Digital

Put your scientific skills to the test with our digital homeworks covering everything from creating PowerPoint presentations to making podcasts and writing wikis to share with your entire class.

If you need help on how to make a podcast or how to set up a wiki there is advice for students and teachers on our website www.collinseducation.com/ks3science

How Science Works

Look out for our HSW icons throughout the Homework Book. This is where you will really show How Science Works in your homework.

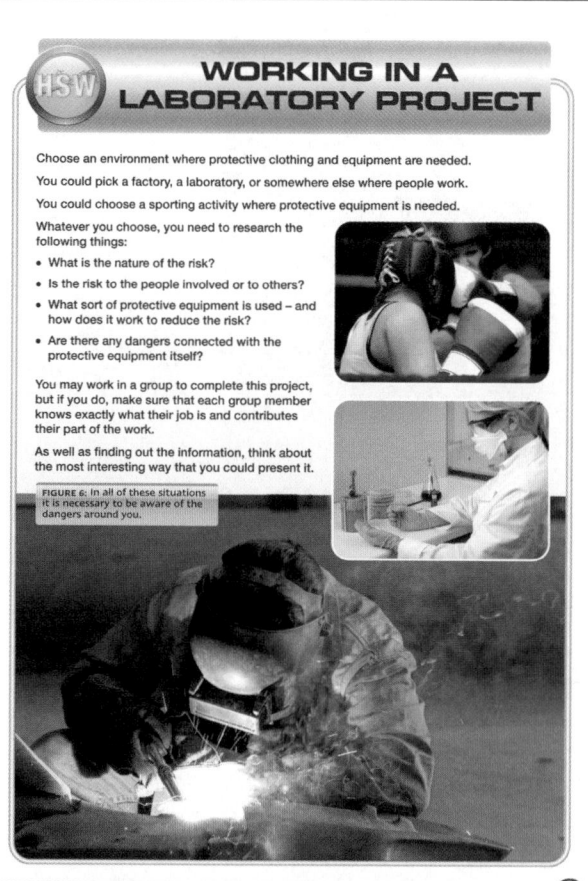

See page 66 of your Student Book

Mid-Topic Projects

About half way through the topic you get a chance to see how much you've learned already by working on a project in groups in class and also at home. Science is put into context as you learn how science relates to the everyday world and has an impact on us all.

Free teaching notes for every mid-topic project are available at www.collinseducation.com/ks3science

Record your progress

At the back of this book you will see your student progress cards. All of the homeworks are levelled into levels 3-4, 5-6 and 7-8. As you work through the book mark which homeworks you are completing for each lesson. As you move through your Key Stage 3 course you will be able to track your progress throughout each topic.

Student Progress Card	Name:		
Organisms, Behaviour and Health	**3-4**	**5-6**	**7-8**
Cell, Tissues and Organs			
Using a microscope			
Studying plant cells			
Studying animal cells			
Designed for a purpose			
Cells, tissues and organs			
Organs and technology			
Reproduction			
Fertilisation and conception			
Courtship			
Becoming an adult			
What are twins?			
How a baby develops			
Birth of the baby			
Reproduction in flowering plants			

Using a microscope

Test yourself

1 Here is a diagram of a simple microscope:

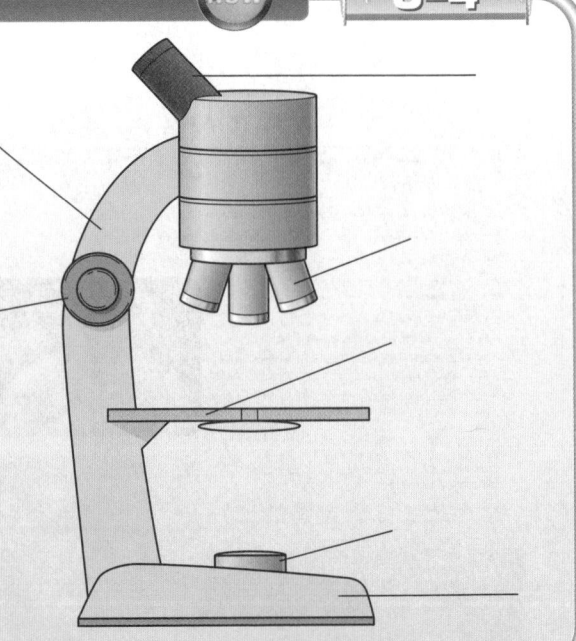

Copy the diagram adding the lines as shown.

Choosing from the list below write the name of each part of the microscope next to its label line.

Try it without looking at the book and then check your answers.

Base
Light
Stage
Arm
Eyepiece
Coarse focus knob
Objective lenses

Creative

2 Imagine that your friend missed the lesson on using microscopes. Your job is to help your friend catch up. Your task is to write out clear step-by-step instructions for how to use a microscope to study a human hair. You must include any safety precautions that are necessary and you must describe everything your friend needs to do – right from setting the microscope up through to looking at the hair through the high power lens.
You could include simple diagrams to make your instructions clearer.

When you have finished your work you could check with someone at home that the instructions are clear enough to follow.

Digital

3 So far you have learned something about the history and use of the light microscope. This activity requires you to do some research about electron microscopes. First of all find out what makes an electron microscope so much more useful than the simple light microscope, concentrate on the benefits rather than the problems such as cost. Your task is to come up with a marketing campaign to show potential customers the benefits of the electron microscope over the light microscope.

An attractive poster would fit the bill nicely here, but if you have the equipment how about writing and performing a podcast?

Studying plant cells

1 Look at this drawing of a typical plant cell. Copy the diagram into your exercise book. Against each label line add the correct name of the part.

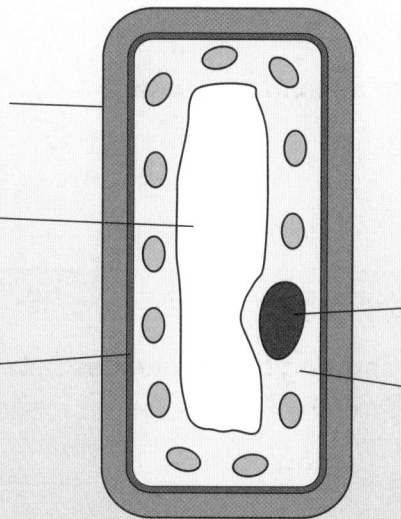

2 Carry out some research into the English scientist Robert Hooke.
Be prepared to make a presentation to the rest of your class.
Make sure that you answer the following questions in your presentation:

When did he live?

Where was he born?

What is his connection with plant cells?

What other areas of science was he involved in?

What is his connection with the Great Fire of London?

3 Your model plant cell has been voted the best in the class. Now you have been asked to write an article for the school magazine about how to build a model cell. Provide step-by-step instructions clearly describing the materials required, together with any safety instructions. Use drawings if they help your explanation.

Remember someone who has not previously done this activity should be able to successfully follow your instructions.

Studying animal cells

Creative

1   Design a poster about plant and animal cells suitable for primary school pupils. The poster will be a visual aid to help them remember what the cells are like so make sure it:

- is mainly based on drawings
- only has essential words with no long sentences
- is simple, colourful and attractive
- is scientifically accurate.

Test yourself

2   Copy and complete this table showing the differences between plant and animal cells. Put a ✔ for present and an ✘ for absent.

Structure	Plant cell	Animal cell
nucleus		
cell wall		
cytoplasm		
chloroplast		
cell membrane		
cell vacuole		

Try this first without referring to your book and then check your answers.

Digital

3   Health and safety is very important when working in a science laboratory. You have recently carried out practical work looking at cells that involves a number of hazards such as:

- working with delicate glass
- working with sharp instruments such as scalpels or needles
- working near hot lamps
- handling human cells etc.

Using your experiences and some research into hazards produce a hazard-warning poster for people using microscopes to look at cells. You can use websites such as Wikipedia to find out more information.

Your poster must clearly:

- name each hazard
- explain the hazard
- explain how to reduce the risk of the hazard.

See pages 12–13 of your Student Book

Designed for a purpose

3-4

Digital

1 As mentioned in your Student Book damage to nerve cells can cause paralysis. Do some research about paralysis and prepare a PowerPoint presentation or a leaflet aimed at the families of people suffering from paralysis.

The kind of information you might want to give could include:

- which types of injury or disease can cause it
- what the symptoms are (i.e. how it affects the body)
- what the possible treatment is, and especially
- how families could help patients cope in everyday life.

One good source of information is the Brain and Spine Foundation (www.brainandspine.org.uk).

5-6

Test yourself

2 Copy and complete this drawing of a sperm cell by labelling the different parts.

For each part explain how it helps the cell to fertilise the egg.

7-8

Creative

3 Put all of the information you have learned about specialised cells into a mind map to help you to learn and remember it. You should try to show a clear link between the design of each cell and its function.

Start at the centre of a blank landscape piece of paper, with a colourful image to represent the subject (remember – a picture is worth a thousand words!).

Also remember – mind maps should be colourful and attractive to encourage people to look at them.

CELLS, TISSUES AND ORGANS PROJECT

Knowledge about how cells, tissues and organs work has enabled many medical advances. Organ transplants are common events as are skin grafts for people with severe burns. Now scientists are working on face transplants! Scientists are also experimenting with growing new layers of skin using stem cells and even growing tissues such as new heart valves. The most amazing example of this work so far is using a live mouse to grow a new human ear!

In class, you are going to create a time line of all the key events in this kind of work.

The time line will be a big wall display and not only will it contain the key events and dates but you will also have newspaper reports and/or pictures to accompany the events.

Your task is to carry out research to try and complete this table.

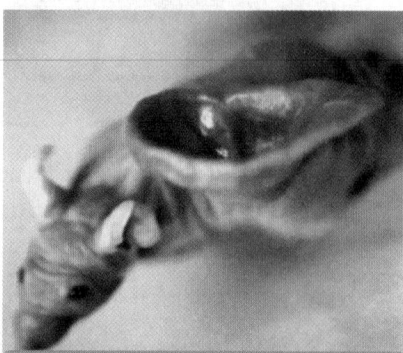

FIGURE 1: This human ear growing on a live mouse is an example of bioengineering.

FIGURE 2: Valve tissue inside a human heart.

Event	Date
First heart transplant	
First kidney transplant	
First lung transplant	
First liver transplant	
First use of heart-lung machine	
First use of kidney dialysis machine	
First skin transplant	
First transplant of cornea of the eye	
First hand transplant	
First face transplant	
First successful growth of new skin	

If you find any other key dates then add them to the table.

As well as researching the dates see if you can find pictures or newspaper reports to accompany the events. A good way of doing this is to search on the websites of British newspapers. To do this type the name of the newspaper, e.g. The Daily Mail into Google and you will find the website. All the newspaper websites have a search box that you can use.

See page 16 of your Student Book

Cells, tissues and organs

Digital  3-4

1 Do some research on cancer and its treatment. Prepare a PowerPoint presentation that covers these areas:

- what cancer means
- the causes of cancer
- how cancer can be treated, and
- how to adapt your lifestyle to try and avoid cancer.

Test yourself  5-6

2 This diagram, taken from page 19 of your Student Book, shows a number of organs of the human body.
Copy and complete the table; naming each organ and stating what system it is part of.

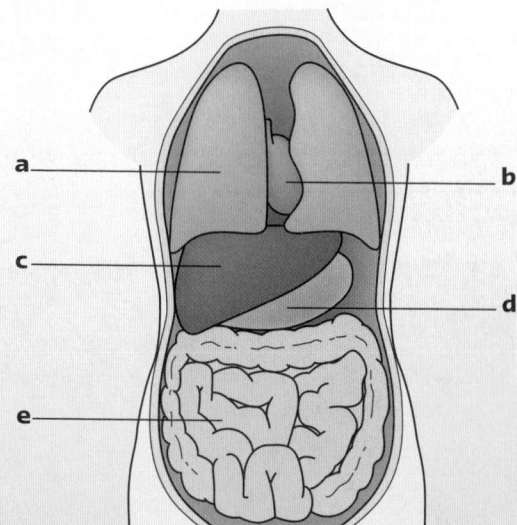

Letter	Name	System
a		
b		
c		
d		
e		

Creative 7-8

3 Design a colourful and informative poster that explains the connection between cells, tissues, organs and systems.

Your task is to start with a muscle cell and end up with the circulatory system. It is important that at the organ and system stages you show what other kinds of tissue are involved in addition to muscle tissue.

You need to be scientifically accurate and at the same time make the poster easy for a wide audience to read.

Organs and technology

1 Copy out the two lists below showing organs of the body and their role.
Use straight lines to match up each organ with its role in the body.

Organ	Role
Brain	pumps blood around the body
Lungs	filter the blood
Heart	coordinates the body's activities
Stomach	get oxygen into the bloodstream
Kidneys	digests food

2 A friend has to go into a hospital for 'open heart surgery'. Your friend is frightened because they have been told that they will be connected to a heart-lung machine. Produce a simple information sheet designed to tell your friend all about the machine and why it is used.

Remember to write it in such a way that it is both informative and reassuring.

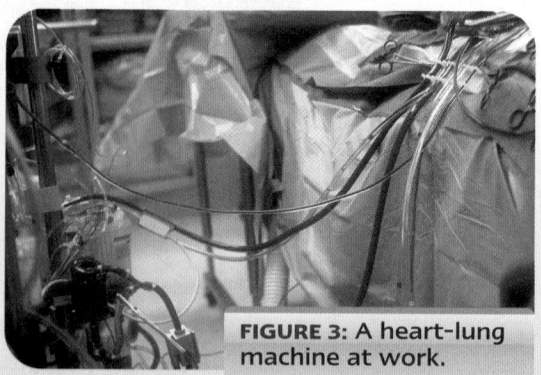

FIGURE 3: A heart-lung machine at work.

3 In 2007, 400 people died whilst waiting for an organ transplant. Carry out some research about organ donation (www.uktransplant.org.uk is a good place to start). Find out about what it means to be a donor, why it is important etc.

Your task is to write a letter to the letters page of a local newspaper as if you are the head of the local hospital. Your letter is aimed at convincing young people (18-25 years) that they should sign up to become organ donors.

Fertilisation and conception

1 Look at this row of letters – each is the first letter of an important structure or event in reproduction. Most of them feature in this photograph, taken with a powerful microscope.

S F O E S C E T

FIGURE 1: Sperm on their way to the ovum.

a What are the male sex cells called?

b What do we call the joining of the male and female sex cells?

c Where is the female sex cell made?

d What is the female sex cell called?

e What do we call the fluid in which sperm swim?

f What do we call the event when the egg implants in the uterus wall?

g What is fertilisation that happens outside the female body?

h Where are the male sex cells made?

Creative   5-6

2 Imagine that you have a test on fertilisation and conception. Your best friend missed this lesson and needs to catch up. Your task is to prepare a summary sheet that will enable your friend to revise quickly and easily. The summary sheet needs to describe the journey of a sperm from the point where it is made all the way until it reaches the egg. This is a summary – so rather than writing everything out as it would be in a book, use diagrams, key words, colours, arrows and so on to present the information in a way that is easy to understand and absorb.

Digital   7-8

3 The UK has the highest rate of teenage pregnancy in Europe (although not in the world where the highest rate is in parts of Africa).

Your task is to do some research and produce a PowerPoint presentation on teenage pregnancy in the UK. The key questions to try to answer are:

- Why do you think we have high numbers of teenage pregnancies in the UK?
- What could we do to reduce these figures?

As well as looking at websites, it would be interesting to research the views of people of different ages for example young people, people of your parents' or carers' age and older people. In your presentation you could separately record the views of these different groups and then at the end, as a summary, present your own considered opinion.

(Wikipedia has a good section on this topic, but if you use it try to pick out a few key points rather than copying out large chunks.)

Courtship

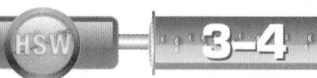
3-4

Creative

1 Produce a mind map to summarise all the different ways that male animals try to attract females. You don't need to include how the methods work, but in each case do try to give an example of an animal that uses that method.

Start at the centre of a blank landscape piece of paper, with a colourful image to represent the subject.

Also remember that mind maps should be colourful and attractive to encourage people to look at them.

5-6

Digital

2 This task is all about researching the many different types of courtship behaviour and turning this information into an entertaining and informative PowerPoint presentation.

You have learned already that animals use sound, scent, display and movement in courtship behaviour. You also know about male territorial behaviour involving fighting.

Create a PowerPoint presentation about courtship behaviour and build in photographs, sounds and even video clips if possible to make the subject come alive.

FIGURE 2: Male kangaroos fight with each other in order to win a mate.

7-8

Test yourself

3 Copy this passage and then fill in the gaps in this account of courtship behaviour. All the answers can be found in your Student Book, but have a go without the book first and then check your answers.

Courtship is not simply about selecting a mate but in fact it is more about selecting the .... and healthiest mate. This is designed to ensure that the .... show similar characteristics. Two males will often .... in order to win the right to mate with a female. The male that wins the female in this kind of contest is called the .... male. This kind of male will often be found with a .... of females. All the females in this group will be .... by this male. This type of reproductive behaviour can lead to many offspring being born with the .... features of the dominant male. In the long term this can make the .... as a whole more likely to survive.

Becoming an adult

3-4

Digital

1 You have learned that becoming an adult is associated with various changes in your body. Beyond the science lab being an adult is often taken to mean being able to do lots of things legally such as drinking alcohol and smoking.

Carry out some research into the legal ages for various activities and be prepared to make a short presentation to the class. You might like to find out the legal age to:

- drink alcohol
- smoke cigarettes
- have sexual intercourse
- vote in a general election
- drive a car
- fight for your country
- take a part-time job, plus any other examples you can think of!

5-6

Test yourself

2 Match up these descriptions of events in the menstrual cycle with the correct diagram illustrating the event.

After three weeks the egg has almost reached the uterus.

After one week an egg is ripening and the uterus is building up.

On day one menstrual bleeding occurs.

After two weeks an egg is released.

a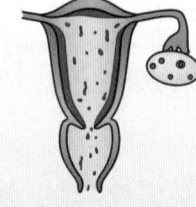

c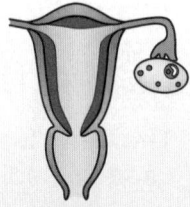

b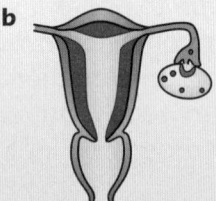

d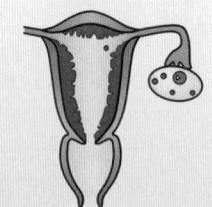

7-8

Creative

3 Some couples have children as soon as they reach the legal age for sexual intercourse (16 years old).

Write an article for a teenage magazine explaining why it would be very difficult for a couple so young to bring up a family. Think about things such as money, jobs, having a home, your friends and so on.

See pages 32–33 of your Student Book

What are twins?

1 This is a creative communication task. You have to explain how the three different types of twin (non-identical, identical and Siamese) are formed, using only pictures to help you explain. You may label the parts of your drawings, or produce a key at the bottom of the page, but you must not use words to explain what is happening.

2 In a SAT question a student is asked to explain how identical twins are formed. Here is his answer:

'A woman releases two eggs and both eggs are fertilised by the same sperm.'

This is the wrong answer. Write the correct response to this question.

What kind of twins would the event the boy described actually produce?

3 The term 'Siamese twins' is no longer commonly used in medical circles.

Carry out some research to find out why the term was originally used for conjoined twins and be prepared to give a short presentation about this to the class. You should try to find out about the lives of the individuals concerned and include this in your presentation.

FIGURE 3: The longest surviving Siamese twins.

REPRODUCTION PROJECT

In Britain around 45 000 IVF treatments (or cycles) are given every year and the average cost is £2 000 each. Nearly three-quarters of these cycles are carried out privately because the NHS has limited resources. Under certain conditions couples can get up to three cycles free on the NHS, although this can vary depending on where you live.

This task is all about looking at one of the biggest factors that influences how widely available new technology is to the population – money.

First of all do some Internet research to find out the cost of a range of operations carried out on the NHS such as heart bypasses. (Go to www.bbc.co.uk/news and search for 'cost of NHS operations'.)

Put these operations in a list, starting with the cheapest at the top. Add the £2000 cost of one IVF cycle into the list too.

Now think about your answers to these questions:

1 Where in the list does IVF come?

2 What would the list look like if you reorganised it to show the operations in order of importance?

3 Where is IVF now and why?

4 Should IVF treatment be free to all the people who need it, no matter what their age, lifestyle and no matter how many cycles they need?

These questions are designed to get you thinking about real issues.

In class you will be asked to work in a group to put together a presentation for or against the following statement:

IVF treatment should be freely available to all on the NHS without any restriction.

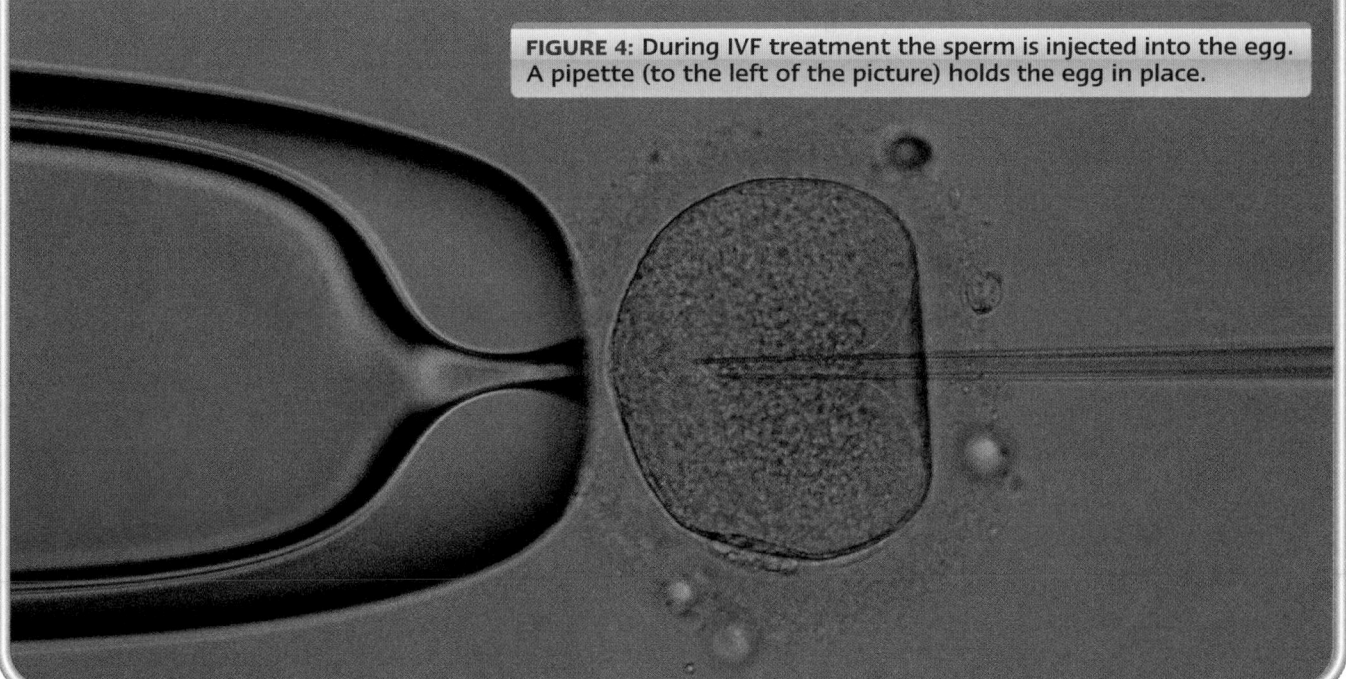

FIGURE 4: During IVF treatment the sperm is injected into the egg. A pipette (to the left of the picture) holds the egg in place.

See page 36 of your Student Book

How a baby develops

1 The length of time that an animal is pregnant is known as the gestation period. Carry out some research to find out the length of the gestation period for a variety of animals. Find photographs or drawings of these animals and create a wall chart timeline to show this information.

Is there a relationship between the size of the animal and the length of its gestation period?

FIGURE 5: Elephants have a long gestation period.

2 Copy and complete this table by matching up the following structures with their correct role.

umbilical cord   uterus wall   amnion   placenta   amniotic fluid

Structure	Role
	contains a very powerful muscle
	protects the foetus
	attaches the foetus to the placenta
	allows the transfer of materials between foetus and mother
	retains fluid and helps to prevent infection

Apart from the structures in this table, what else helps to protect the developing foetus?

3 Using the information from your Student Book, design an information sheet for pregnant mothers. The purpose of the sheet will be to explain how the placenta works and it should therefore show the dangers of smoking, drinking and taking drugs when pregnant.

Try to include a simple diagram showing how materials might pass between the foetus and the mother.

Your target audience will have a wide range of ability so your sheet must be easy to read and attractive enough to encourage people to read it.

Birth of the baby

1 Given below is a series of starts and ends to sentences. Decide which start goes with which ending and write out the complete correct sentences.

A human pregnancy…	…usually pointing downwards.
The head of the baby is…	…it is delivered.
During labour…	…the mother goes into labour.
When a baby is born we say …	…is usually 38 weeks.
When a baby is ready to be born …	…is known as the waters breaking.
The passing out of amniotic fluid…	…the uterus starts to contract.

2 Draw a poster that explains why a breech birth is so much more difficult than a headfirst birth, and what can be done to turn the baby the right way around before birth.

Think about how you can show this information with relatively few words.

3 Some women choose to have what is called a water birth. Carry out some research to find out all you can about water births. Use your research to complete the following two tasks:

- Prepare a fact sheet that could be available in a doctor's surgery; this would need to explain what a water birth is and give the possible benefits compared to a non-water birth.

- Water births often take place in the woman's home although they can also take place in hospital by special arrangement. Bearing this in mind, if there was a big rise in the number of water births, explain how this might affect hospitals and maternity staff.

FIGURE 6: Water births are becoming more popular.

Reproduction in flowering plants

Creative — 3-4

1 Produce an attractive poster showing the names of all the parts of a typical flower. Imagine that your poster is designed for a primary school classroom and think carefully about what will make it suitable for this kind of situation.

FIGURE 7: Can you name all the parts of a flower?

Test yourself — 5-6

2 In a SAT question a student was asked to explain the difference between pollination and fertilisation. Here is what he wrote:

> 'Pollination occurs only in plants and fertilisation occurs only in animals.'

- Which part of his sentence is correct?
- Which part is incorrect?
- Explain why this part is incorrect.

FIGURE 8: An example of insect pollination.

Digital — HSW — 7-8

3 This question builds upon what you learned about wind– and insect– pollinated flowers. You have probably looked at the differences between the flowers themselves but what about the pollen grains? How are some suitable for being carried by the wind and others by animals?

Your task is firstly to carry out some research on pollen grains using library books and/or the Internet. Having gathered some information, prepare a short illustrated presentation for your class about the differences between these different types of pollen grains.

See pages 42–43 of your Student Book

Safety in the laboratory

1 Peter burns a piece of crispbread to find out how much energy is stored in it. Energy from the burning crispbread raises the temperature of the water in the test tube.

  a Describe the way Peter has arranged the apparatus so that he is working safely.

  b Can you suggest a way in which Peter could make his experiment even safer?

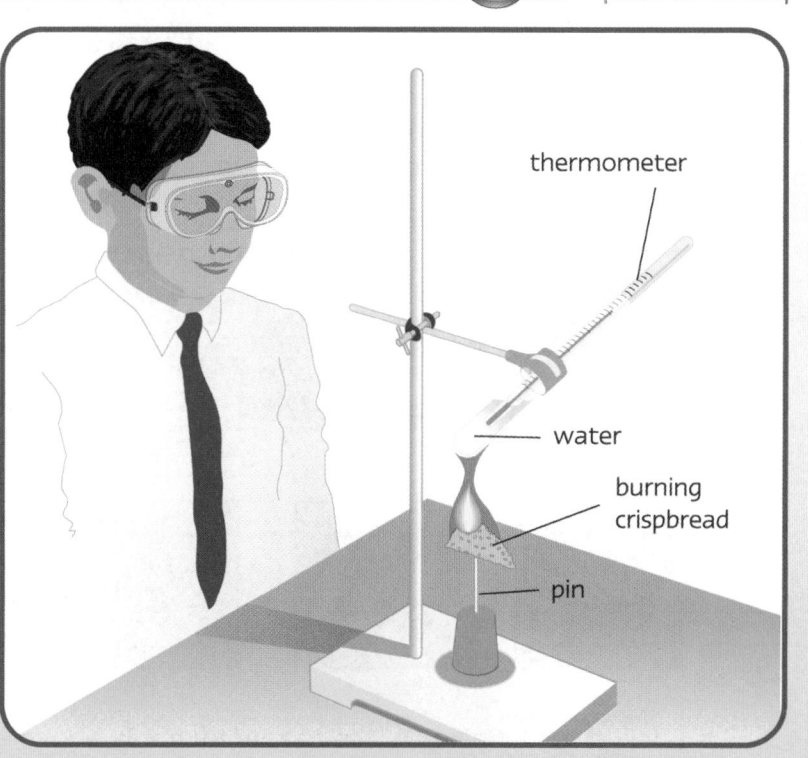

thermometer

water

burning crispbread

pin

2 Many accidents happen at home, especially in the kitchen. Prepare an information leaflet about ways of ensuring that all members of a family are kept safe in the kitchen.

3 Use the Internet to research accident statistics for the last five years. Choose a category such as: road accidents, accidents in the home or accidents to children. Decide on an interesting way to present your results.

Hazard warning signs

1 The question below has been answered by two different students – one in red and one in blue.

QUESTION: 'Many chemicals are dangerous if not used carefully. Read the **two** hazard descriptions. Look at the hazard labels. Draw a line from each description to the correct label.'

Hazard descriptions

POISONOUS
This will cause damage if swallowed

CORROSIVE
This can attack or dissolve many things

a Look at the labelling of the hazard symbols above – what would you say to Sarah who answered the question in red?

b What would you say to James who wrote his answers in blue?

2 You are going on a visit with your science teacher to a nearby primary school to talk to students in Y5 and Y6 about staying safe from harmful chemicals. Design a simple booklet that could be used to help explain to these children what hazard symbols are and to show them some of the more common ones that they might come across. Remember to write clearly and use lots of illustrations.

3 Design a Hazcard for a chemical that you might find in the school laboratory. Decide what information should be on the card and then use books and the Internet to find out as much about that chemical as you can. When you have found the information, present it clearly in a way that is easy to read and understand.

The Bunsen burner

3-4

Creative

1 Write an instruction leaflet for students who are new to working in a laboratory on how to use the Bunsen burner. Make sure you include the information they need on how to work safely.

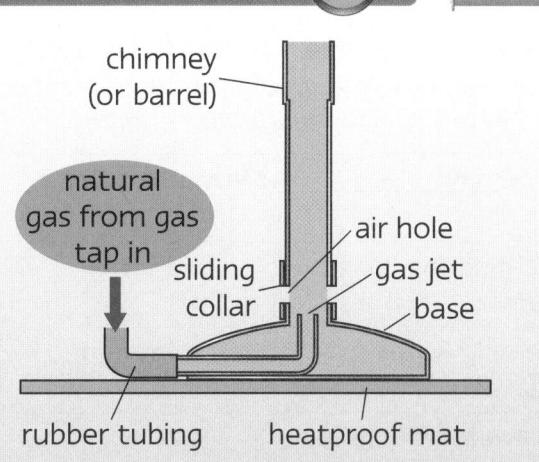

5-6

Test yourself

2 The diagrams show two Bunsen burners. One burner has the air hole closed, and the other has the air hole open.

a Explain why opening the air hole of a Bunsen burner makes the flame hotter.

b Natural gas is methane, CH_4. It is burned in a Bunsen burner. Complete the word equation for the chemical reaction in the clear blue flame.

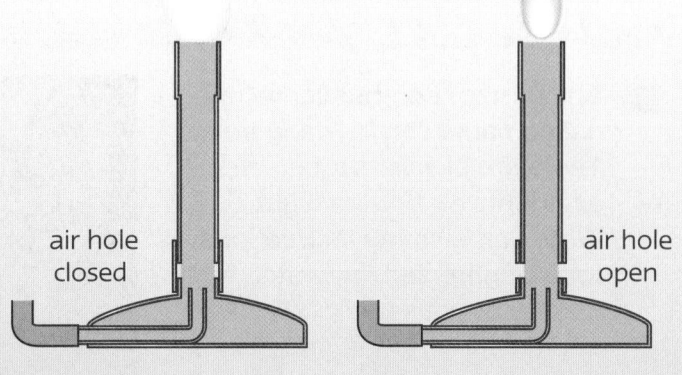

methane + ... ➡ .... + ...

7-8

Digital

3 Research the life and work of Robert Bunsen. Find out all that you can about him and his work and prepare a PowerPoint presentation. Robert Bunsen lived from 1811 to 1899 – so he lived for most of the nineteenth century. Find another scientist who lived in the nineteenth century and add some key facts about his/her life and work to your presentation.

FIGURE 1: Robert Bunsen.

The best flame

1 Copy and complete the table below to show which flame you would use in each example; how you would produce this flame by opening or closing the air hole, and why you have made that choice.

Activity	Flame required	Position of air hole	Reason for choice of flame
Lighting the Bunsen burner			
Heating water in a beaker			
Leaving the Bunsen burner alight whilst you prepare your next experiment			

   a What is the correct scientific term for burning?

   b Which colour of flame shows that combustion is complete?

Creative
5-6

2 Any form of combustion with a naked flame can be dangerous. There are always a lot of accidents on bonfire night. Write some safety instructions for a bonfire and fireworks display at your school. Think about safety for the organisers, the visitors and the people attending the party.

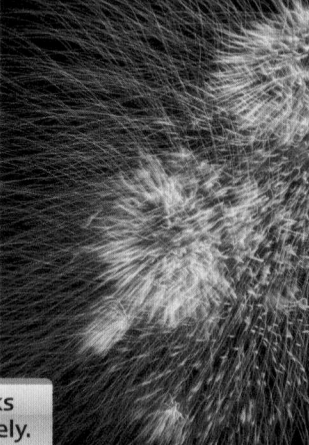

FIGURE 2: Fireworks are fun if used safely.

Digital
7-8

3 Research the history of bonfire night. What were Guy Fawkes and his associates trying to do and how much of the science behind their plot can you explain?

Prepare a PowerPoint presentation that links the science and the history.

What makes things burn?

1 The fire brigade recommends that you put out a fire in a chip pan in your kitchen by placing a damp tea towel over the top of the pan to smother the flames.

Draw a safety poster to explain this – include the fire triangle on your poster to help with your explanation.

2 Some students carried out an experiment to see how long a candle would burn when a bell jar was placed over the top of it.

a What are the **three** things needed for a fire to burn?

b What is the name of the diagram we use to show these three things?

c Draw the diagram that you have named in your answer to **b**.

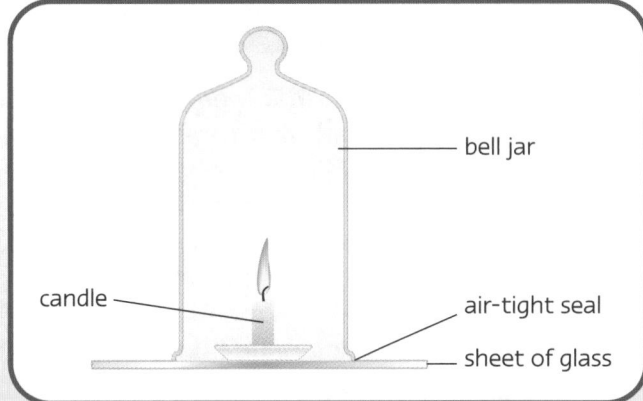

d Explain, using the fire triangle, why the candle only burned for a short time when placed under the bell jar in this way.

e Predict what would happen to the length of time a candle of the same size would burn if it was placed under a glass container that was half the volume of the bell jar.

f Which features of the apparatus shown in the diagram would need to be repeated with the half volume container to make sure that it was a fair test?

3 'Burning is a chemical reaction – the scientific name for burning is combustion.'

Prepare a PowerPoint presentation to explain this statement in as much detail as you can.

Things you might like to include:

- which part of the air is needed for combustion

- the products of combustion

- types of fuels that allow combustion

- examples of combustion reactions.

FIGURE 3: Science is everywhere; even in birthday cake!

Putting out a fire

1   **a** What is the name of the gas used to put out fires?

    b What makes this gas suitable for putting out fires?

    c What is the role of carbon dioxide in a soda-acid fire extinguisher?

    d Why is it unsafe to use water to put out an electrical fire?

    e If you discovered a fire in your home, what **four** steps should you take?

Digital   5–6

2   You have found out that there is a plan to build an oil storage depot near to your home. There is to be a public meeting to debate this proposal and anyone who lives nearby is invited to attend and give a short presentation setting out their views for or against. Prepare the presentation you would make at this meeting. Remember to include as much scientific fact as you can to add strength to your argument. Use the Internet to find out more about the size of oil depots and what safety precautions they take.

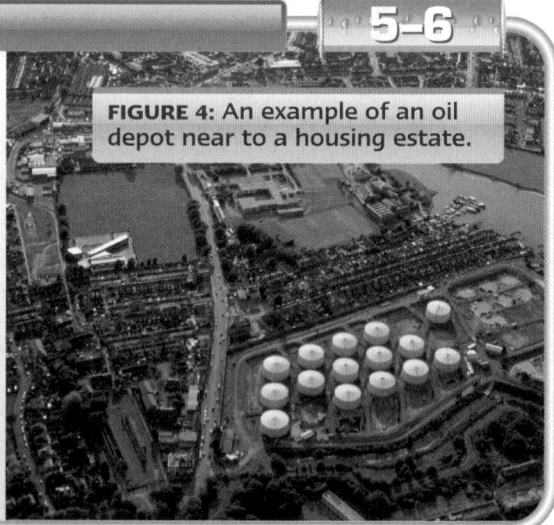

FIGURE 4: An example of an oil depot near to a housing estate.

Creative   7–8

3   As well as the fire brigade, specially trained scientists often attend fires to look for clues that might tell them how the fire started – especially if there is any suspicion that the fire was started deliberately.

Imagine that you are one of these forensic scientists. You have been called to a fire in a factory that makes carpets. The whole building and everything in it has been destroyed by the intense heat of the fire. The charred remains are soaked with all the water that the fire brigade had to use to put out the blaze. What clues would you look for? How would you form an opinion about whether or not the fire was started deliberately?

Write the report that such a scientist might produce – decide what you would look for and how you would decide whether it was an accident or something more sinister!

Fire precautions at school

3-4

Test yourself

1

  a What are the **two** chemicals in a soda-acid fire extinguisher?

  b Write the equation for the reaction between these two chemicals.

  c Why are the chemicals in a soda-acid fire extinguisher kept apart until the extinguisher is needed?

  d Why would it be very dangerous if a fire broke out in a school at 10am on a Wednesday?

  e Why would it be worse if a fire broke out in a school at 10pm on a Saturday?

FIGURE 5: A soda-acid fire extinguisher.

5-6

Creative

2 Conduct a survey of the fire safety equipment in your school. Find out how many fire extinguishers there are and of what types and where they are to be found. What other safety equipment (such as fire blankets and sand buckets, fire doors and safety notices) is available. How is the fire alarm activated? What is the procedure for everyone to follow? How long does it take to clear the building when the fire alarm sounds? Prepare a report of your findings.

fire extinguisher

FIRE BLANKET
MODEL: 1m X 1m

PULL TAPES
TO REMOVE
BLANKET

COVER BURNING
MATERIAL
COMPLETELY

SWITCH OFF HEAT
LEAVE COVERED UNTIL COOL
DISCARD AFTER USE

fire blanket

sand bucket

7-8

Digital

3 Look at the questions raised in question 2 about fire safety in your school. Evaluate how safe you think your school is and produce a PowerPoint presentation which could explain to new parents the steps that are taken to keep their children safe from fire risks at school – and the responsibility of every student to help keep the whole school safe.

Acids and alkalis

1 The question below is part of a SAT paper question. Look at the answers that a student has written and decide whether they are correct, giving a reason for your answer.

The chart is taken from a bottle of *Johnson's pH5.5 Facial Wash*.

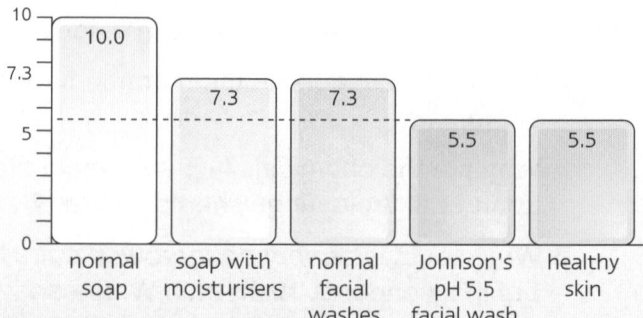

a From the information in the chart give a substance that is:

  i almost neutral – *normal soap*

  ii most alkaline – *healthy skin*

State whether the student has answered correctly or incorrectly and explain why.

b Which **one** of these statements describes Johnson's facial wash?

  It is neutral   It is very alkaline   It is slightly alkaline   It is slightly acidic

State whether the student has answered correctly or incorrectly and explain why.

2 Your class has just carried out an experiment using hydrochloric acid. Students at your local primary school think this is dangerous. Design a cartoon sketch showing how everyday acids are used and any dangers involved with them.

3 You may have heard the term 'acid rain'. You will certainly learn about it in your science lessons and maybe in other subjects like geography as well. Come to the next lesson with **five** facts about acid rain. You will find a lot of information on the Internet to help you. Your five facts, along with everyone else's facts, can be used to make a whole-class fact file. You could maybe do this as a whole-class wiki. Think about these areas when looking for your facts:

- What makes the rain acidic?
- Is acid rain a strong acid?
- Does acid rain do any harm; if so what does it harm?
- Can the harm done by acid rain be put right again and, if so, how?
- Do humans do things that cause acid rain?
- Is there anything that we as individuals can do to help reduce the problem of acid rain?

See pages 64–65 of your Student Book

HSW

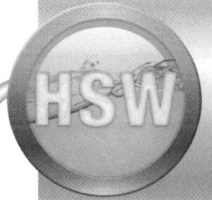

WORKING IN A LABORATORY PROJECT

Choose an environment where protective clothing and equipment are needed.

You could pick a factory, a laboratory, or somewhere else where people work.

You could choose a sporting activity where protective equipment is needed.

Whatever you choose, you need to research the following things:

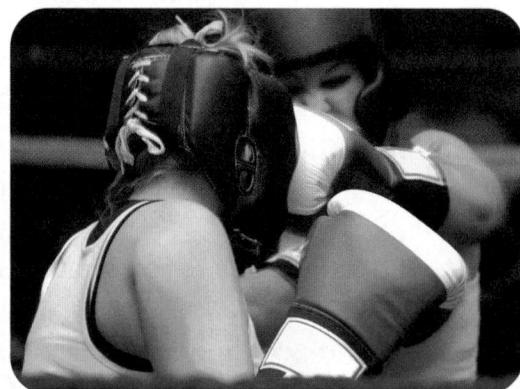

- What is the nature of the risk?
- Is the risk to the people involved or to others?
- What sort of protective equipment is used – and how does it work to reduce the risk?
- Are there any dangers connected with the protective equipment itself?

You may work in a group to complete this project, but if you do, make sure that each group member knows exactly what their job is and contributes their part of the work.

As well as finding out the information, think about the most interesting way that you could present it.

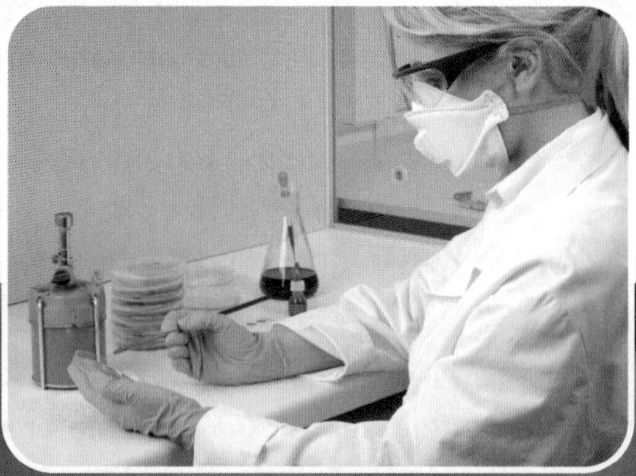

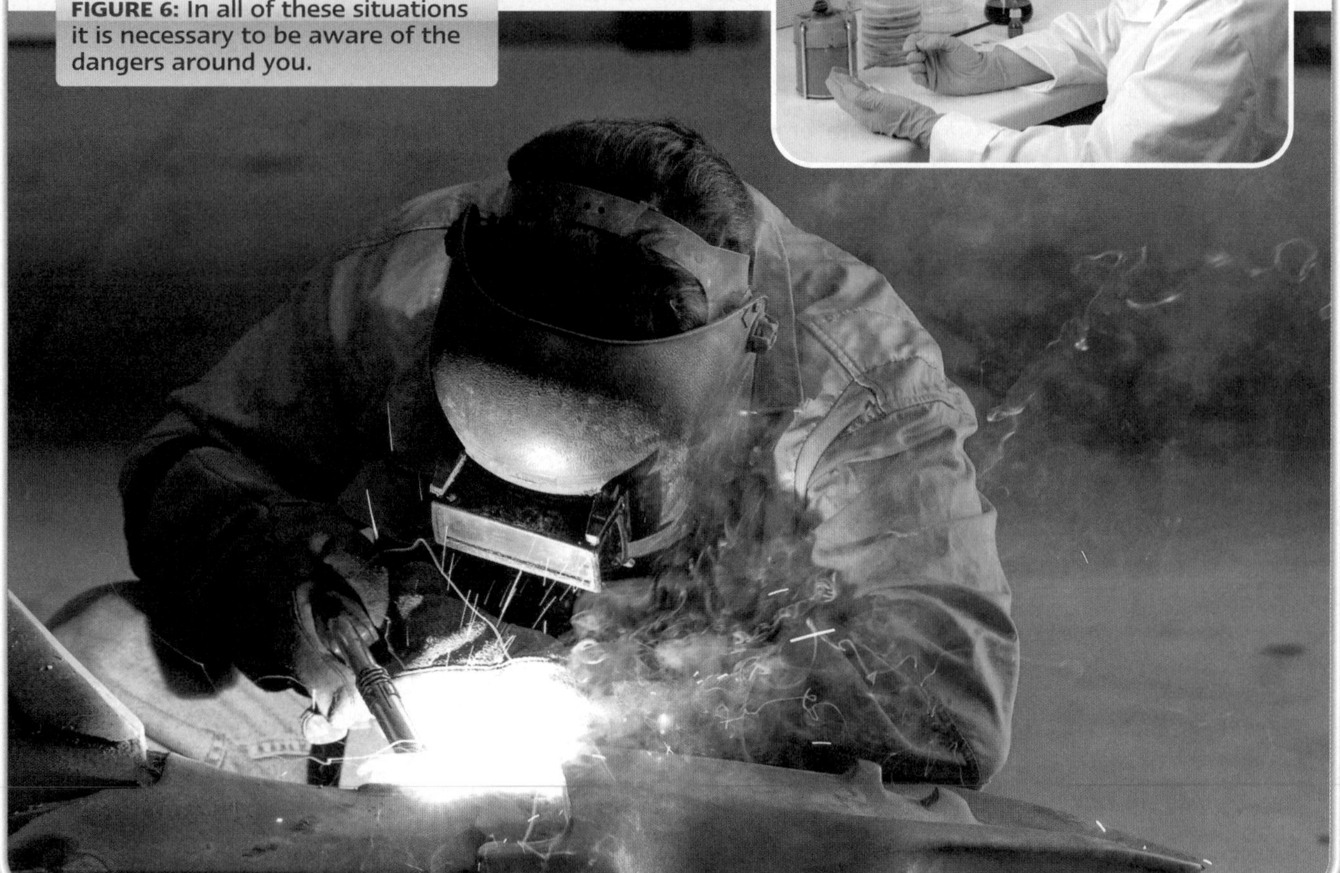

FIGURE 6: In all of these situations it is necessary to be aware of the dangers around you.

See page 66 of your Student Book

Indicators

1 You have been given the instructions for making an indicator from red cabbage – unfortunately the instructions were on strips of card that have been jumbled up.

A Warm the boiling tube with red cabbage and ethanol by putting the boiling tube into warm water.

B Turn off the gas to put out the Bunsen burner.

C Put shredded red cabbage into a boiling tube and cover it with ethanol.

D Put on your safety glasses.

E Heat about 300 cm³ of water in a large beaker until it boils.

F Filter the solution to remove the remains of red cabbage.

G Set up a tripod and gauze on a heat-proof mat, place the beaker of water on the gauze and carefully light a Bunsen burner.

a Put the cards into the correct order so that you can safely begin the experiment. Write the letter for each statement to show the order in which they should go. Start with Step 1.

b Some of these steps are to make sure that you are working safely. Select **two** steps that you think will help you to work safely.

 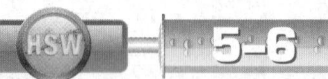

2 Write an instruction leaflet to enable other students to use litmus paper. Give examples of everyday acids and alkalis and show what colour the litmus paper would turn. Don't forget to include and explain neutral substances, and to include advice for working safely.

3 Research the other plants that can be used to make indicator solutions in the same way as red cabbage. Can you find out which one is the best? How can you decide which is the best?

See pages 68–69 of your Student Book

Weak and strong

1 a A group of students tested some liquids with Universal indicator. They have not completed their results table. From your knowledge of acids and alkalis complete the table for them.

Substance	Colour of Universal indicator solution	pH	Acid or alkali
Water		7	
Lemon juice		4	
Paint stripper	Dark purple		
Hair shampoo		8	
Car battery acid			
Vinegar			

STRONG ACIDS	1	
	2	
	3	red
	4	
WEAK ACIDS	5	orange
	6	yellow
NEUTRAL	7	green
WEAK ALKALIS	8	blue
	9	blue-purple
	10	
	11	
STRONG ALKALIS	12	purple
	13	
	14	

b Read these statements about acids and alkalis then decide which are true and which are false.

i Acids are more dangerous than alkalis.

ii Alkaline solutions are always safe to drink.

iii If you put a small amount of a strong acid into a beaker of water then it becomes a weak acid.

iv Pure water is neutral – rainwater is not always neutral as it is not always pure water.

2 Many cosmetic products claim to have a particular pH value. Find as many as you can of these and produce a presentation about the claims these products make, how you would test the claims and how you would compare them with other products of the same kind. Can you find out why they claim to be a particular pH value?

3 It is easy to get confused with the difference between strong and weak and concentrated and dilute solutions of acids and alkalis. Can you think of an easy way to remember which is which and what each term really means that you could present to help others understand this difference? You could choose a poster, a cartoon strip, an easy to remember poem or even a song. Make sure you include information about pH values.

The pH meter

1 Gardeners often want to change the pH of their soil so that a particular plant will grow well. Design an eye-catching label for a product that will make a soil more acidic. Include some information on the pH to show that this is a scientifically-based product.

2 **a** What is the name of the apparatus in the picture?

b Explain why, in some situations, using this apparatus (rather than litmus paper or Universal indicator) would be a better way of finding out if a solution was acid or alkali.

c What is meant by the term 'buffer solution'?

d Which of these liquids would be best to use as a buffer solution for a pH meter? Explain your choice.

Liquid	pH value
Alcohol	7
Dilute hydrochloric acid	2
Distilled water	7
Vinegar	3
Sodium hydroxide solution	11

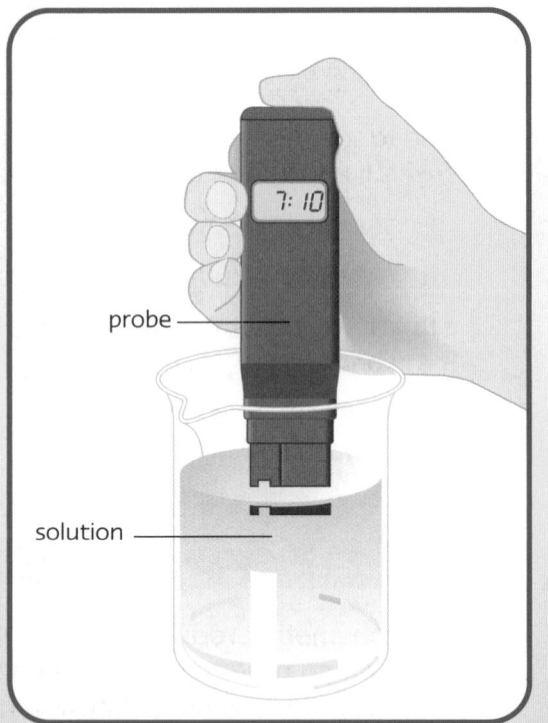

probe

solution

3 Acid conditions such as peat bogs often preserve things for very long periods of time. Find out about something that has been preserved in this way – when and where it was found, how old it was believed to be and so on – and be ready to present what you have found out to the class in the next lesson. You can use PowerPoint or any other way of presenting your findings.

See pages 72–73 of your Student Book

Neutralisation

1 Use the idea of neutralisation as a battle between the H soldiers and the OH soldiers on page 74 of your Student Book. Draw a cartoon strip or poster explaining what happens when an acid and an alkali meet up. Show the difference between when there are the same numbers of H soldiers and OH soldiers and when there are more OH soldiers than H soldiers.

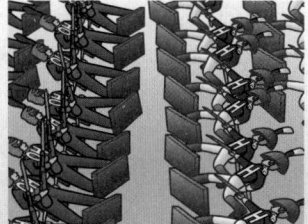 

2 Find out what you can about a real-life process where it may be important to keep the pH at a particular level. You could use cloth dyeing as in the Student Book – or, better still, find out about something else. Think about food processing such as yoghurt or cheese making or the manufacture of paint or fertilisers. Does pH matter for any of these processes – if so, why? Maybe pH does not matter but some other condition needs to be controlled – you could report on that too! Your teacher will set up a wiki for you to record your findings.

3 The table below shows the results of adding alkali to 10 cm³ of acid.

  a Describe **two** methods that could have been used to obtain these results.

  b Plot these results on a graph and draw a smooth curve. Take care to label your axes correctly.

  c On the same axes sketch the curve that you think would show the results if the experiment was repeated with the same solutions but starting with twice the volume of acid.

Volume of alkali added (cm³)	pH of resulting mixture
0.0	5.0
2.0	5.0
4.0	5.0
6.0	5.5
8.0	6.0
10.0	7.0
12.0	8.0
14.0	8.5
16.0	9.0
18.0	9.0
20.0	9.0

Neutralisation in action

1 The makers of 'Happy Tummy' indigestion tablets would like you to produce an advertisement for them to go out on local radio. You have one minute in which to persuade people to buy this product to cure their indigestion.

Write a script for this advert and remember to include some good scientific reasons why 'Happy Tummy' is the best.

2 **a** What is the name of the acid that is found in our stomachs?

b What would you expect the pH of hydrochloric acid to be?

c Indigestion is caused by too much stomach acid. Indigestion tablets work by neutralising excess stomach acid. What would you expect the pH of an indigestion tablet to be?

d If you put a crushed indigestion tablet into a test tube of hydrochloric acid, a chemical reaction takes place.

Look at the word equation for this reaction:

magnesium carbonate + hydrochloric acid ➡️
magnesium chloride + carbon dioxide + water

   i   What sort of reaction is this?

   ii Can you use the word equation to explain why the mixture fizzes?

   iii If you put your hand over the test tube while this reaction is taking place, what do you expect to feel?

— hydrochloric acid

crushed indigestion tablet

3 What are the potential risks to the environment of burning coal to produce electricity in a power station? How can these risks be reduced as far as possible? What are the advantages of coal-fired power stations that make us want to go on taking the risks? Prepare a presentation on the advantages and disadvantages of coal-fired power stations and **one** other way of generating electricity.

Particle World

3–4

Test yourself

1 **a** Draw **three** diagrams to show the arrangement of particles in a solid, a liquid and a gas. You might find it easier to draw your diagrams in boxes.

b Are these statements about solids, liquids and gases true or false?

    i Solids have a fixed shape because the particles are arranged in a regular pattern.

    ii Liquids can easily be compressed.

    iii In a solid the particles are far apart.

    iv Particles in a gas have more energy than particles in a solid.

    v Particles in a liquid can slide past each other; this is why liquids can be poured.

Creative

5–6

2 'Liquids cannot be compressed, gases can.' Use this statement to explain why car brake pipes are filled with a liquid and why it is dangerous to let air get into the brake pipes.

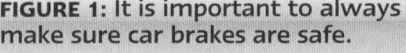

FIGURE 1: It is important to always make sure car brakes are safe.

Write and draw a road safety leaflet encouraging drivers to have their brakes checked regularly. Make sure you include all the science about the particles in gases and liquids so that drivers can understand why they need to make sure their brakes are safe.

Digital

7–8

3 The way that particles behave explains a lot of things we might experience in all sorts of situations. Can you prepare a presentation that explains – using what you know about particles – at least two of these things?

Why your breath seems warm if you breathe on your hands, but cold if you press your lips together and blow.

Why if you heat a plastic bottle full of liquid it might crack.

Why cooking oil straight from the fridge would pour more slowly than if the bottle had been standing somewhere very warm.

Why chocolate melts.

You may want to compile your presentation into a wiki, which you can share with the rest of the class.

Our watery world

1 When you buy ice cream in the supermarket it is stored in a very cold freezer. Produce a short Powerpoint presentation to describe what happens to the ice cream from taking it out of the shop freezer to getting it safely stored in your freezer at home. Remember to use proper scientific words to describe any changes of state.

FIGURE 2: Do you know the science behind ice cream?

Test yourself

2 Some students predicted that water would evaporate faster if the surrounding air temperature were higher. To investigate their prediction they placed some water in containers in two different rooms.

a Give **two** factors they should keep the same to make their investigation fair.

b They recorded the mass of the water and the container in room 1 and room 2 every day for 5 days. The table shows their results.

time (days)	mass of water and container (g)	
	room 1	**room 2**
0	100	100
1	92	85
2	80	72
3	72	54
4	60	45
5	46	30

The data shown in their table is **not** sufficient to test their prediction. Explain why.

c The students then decide to draw a graph of their results. Can you suggest **three** things that would be important to remember when drawing a graph of both of these sets of results on the same axes?

Creative

3 Imagine you are a water molecule. Produce a cartoon strip about a day in your life. Include all the physical changes that you undergo in a day and make sure you explain what causes those changes.

Spreading out

1 What is the proper scientific name for the way particles spread out?

What change of state has to happen before this spreading out can begin?

If some perfume were spilled at the front of your classroom the people at the back of the room would be the last to smell it. Can you explain why?

FIGURE 3: If you spilled perfume who would be the last to smell it and why?

2 When you put some concentrated orange squash into water what happens?

Draw a poster or a cartoon strip that you could use to explain the science behind what you would see to some Year 6 students who are visiting your school.

FIGURE 4: How do the orange squash particles mix with the water?

3 At airports you can often see specially trained dogs moving amongst the luggage and around the passengers. Prepare a presentation to explain what they are doing – and what it has got to do with particles!

How does heat change things?

1 Are chemical changes usually reversible or irreversible?

Which of these changes are irreversible?

   i   Boiling an egg.

   ii   Melting an ice cube.

   iii   Burning a piece of wood.

   iv   Dissolving salt in water.

   v   Boiling water to make steam.

Give **one** example of a reversible change that might happen whilst you are cooking a meal.

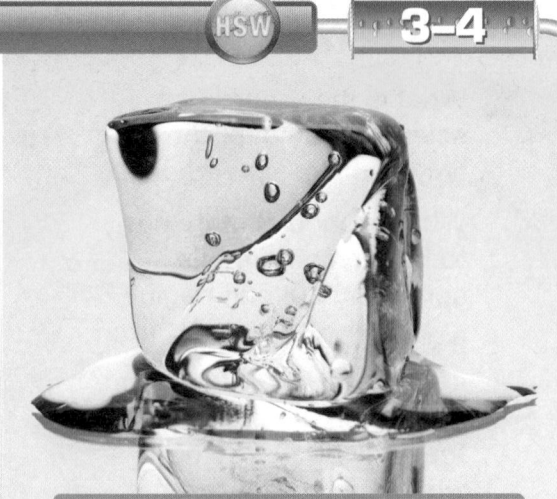

FIGURE 5: When an ice cube melts is it a reversible or irreversible change?

2 Heat can cause physical changes of state or bring about irreversible chemical change. Produce an information leaflet explaining the difference. Use **two** examples such as a melting ice cube and a forest fire – or choose different examples if you prefer.

FIGURE 6: What changes of state occur during a forest fire?

3 Think about what you had for lunch today or for dinner yesterday, or your favourite meal. Imagine you are making a TV cookery programme with a difference! Prepare a script that would tell the viewers not only how to cook your favourite dish – but also explain the physical and chemical changes that take place whilst the cooking is happening. Your teacher will set up a wiki for all the cooking chemistry recipes produced by the whole class so that other classes can access them too. You might like to prepare a video clip in which you explain about the science behind your dinner and put that on the wiki as well.

How does the mass change?

Test yourself

1 What causes copper sulphate crystals to have their attractive blue colour?

Why are grape vines sometimes sprayed with copper sulphate solution?

Why do you sometimes find a small packet of crystals inside the box of something you have bought? What are these crystals called?

What substance that we all have in our diet has a crystal structure?

Can you suggest why some people put a few grains of rice into the bottom of a saltcellar?

FIGURE 7: A solution of copper sulphate can produce these crystals.

FIGURE 8: Inside a salt crystal.

Creative

2 When magnesium ribbon burns it turns to a whitish ash. This ash has a greater mass than the ribbon had at the beginning. This is quite a difficult thing to imagine! Can you find a way of explaining why this happens that would be very easy to understand? You could present your ideas as a cartoon or storyboard – but be sure to include some illustrations that will help to explain what happens.

Digital

3 Our ideas about combustion and the composition of air have changed a lot over the years. Find out what you can about two scientists called Antoine Lavoisier and Joseph Priestley. How do their ideas each compare with what we think now?

FIGURE 9: Antoine Lavoisier.

See pages 92–93 of your Student Book

PARTICLES AND REACTIONS PROJECT

Air ships and hot air balloons both rely on gases and the way that gas particles behave to enable them to fly successfully.

Find out as much as you can about the design of both and what the similarities and differences are. Use the information to prepare an information pack to encourage people to travel by airship or hot air balloon. Include:

- how designs of air ships and hot air balloons have changed since they were both developed
- how and why these changes in design have taken place
- what the safety features of both are
- how the safety features have changed.

FIGURE 10: How do air ships fly?

FIGURE 11: Hot air balloons rely on gases to fly.

See page 94 of your Student Book

Chemical reactions

Creative

1 Draw a poster – divide your sheet of paper in half and on one side give an example of a physical change of state and on the other side an example of a chemical reaction.

Think about the important differences between chemical reactions and physical changes of state; make sure that your poster explains these differences as well as you can.

Test yourself

2 Give **two** examples of things that you might look for if you wanted to know if a chemical reaction was taking place.

Explain **one** difference between chemical reactions and physical changes of state.

What is the special name for the chemical reaction between an acid and an alkali?

Can you give **one** example of this type of reaction?

Digital

7-8

3 In the south of Italy near Naples there is a famous volcano called Vesuvius. It has erupted in the past and once destroyed the cities of Pompeii and Herculaneum. Find out all that you can and prepare a PowerPoint presentation on historical eruptions and how the volcano is monitored today. You may like to find a video of a volcanic eruption to show to your class.

FIGURE 12: Mount Etna is a volcano near to Italy in Sicily. It is still an active volcano.

Fizzy reactions

1 What is the proper scientific word for 'fizzy'?

Describe what you would see if you put some chalk into a beaker of acid.

What is the name of the gas given off in this chemical reaction?

Can you give another example of a reaction that gives off this gas?

What is the name of the gas that all living things need to take in?

Creative
5-6

2 All fizzy drinks contain carbon dioxide. Many people think that if a liquid contains a gas it will be lighter – have less mass – than the same volume of liquid without any gas dissolved in it. Can you think of a way you could use bottles of fizzy drink to illustrate the fact that liquid with dissolved carbon dioxide is heavier than the same volume of liquid without any gas? Produce a cartoon strip to explain your ideas.

Digital
7-8

3 Use the Internet to research which fuel is used in rockets, how it is stored and what the safety considerations are. Try searching for rockets on the NASA website (www.nasa.gov) to see what information is available. Present your findings in a PowerPoint presentation for the rest of the class.

FIGURE 13: What chemical reactions happen in order for a rocket to fly?

See pages 98–99 of your Student Book

More about burning

Creative

1 Draw a picture of a birthday cake with candles on it.

You now know quite a lot about the science that you can see in this picture.

Put some text boxes on your picture describing some of that science.

You might include:

- what happens when a candle burns

- whether baking the cake was a chemical reaction or a physical change of state – and how you know this

- how the energy stored in the cake came originally from the Sun

- how many calories are stored in a cake – or a slice of cake – and how much of the daily intake needed for someone your age is contained in a slice of cake.

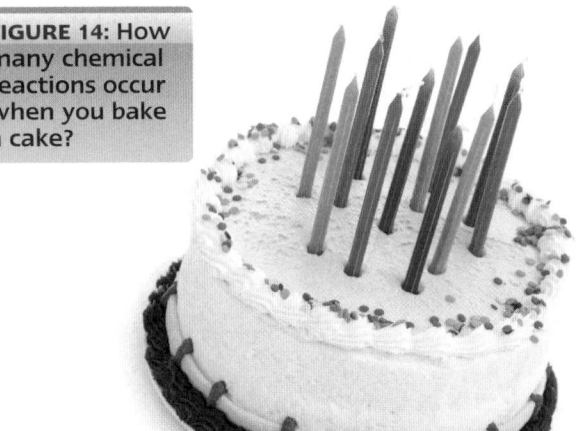

FIGURE 14: How many chemical reactions occur when you bake a cake?

Test yourself

2 What always happens to the mass of a substance when it burns in air? Why is it sometimes difficult to see this change in mass happening?

Complete the word equation for magnesium burning in air:

Magnesium + ... ➝ ....

What fraction of the air around us is made up of the gas that is needed for combustion?

What is the name of the gas that makes up about 80% of the air?

Explain what happens to this gas when we breathe in and out.

Digital

3 Oxyacetylene cutting torches are one way of cutting through metals. Lasers are another method. Find out first of all what 'laser' stands for and then prepare a presentation of your findings on the history and use of lasers.

FIGURE 15: A cutting torch.

Everyday chemistry

Creative

3-4

1 Take a large sheet of paper and divide it into four quarters. In each quarter draw and write a description of an everyday chemical reaction that you might find at home. Think about the ones on pages 102 and 103 of your Student Book – but think about some of the others you have met in other parts of the book or in earlier lessons as well.

FIGURE 16: Can you explain the chemistry behind these everyday reactions?

Test yourself

5-6

2 Why are some adhesives only temporary?
Give an example of an adhesive that you would not want to last forever!

What is the usual pH of soap and detergent products?

Explain how detergents separate dirt and grease from our skin and our clothes.

Suggest why some cleaning products work better the hotter the water, but others work best at around 40 °C.

Digital

7-8

3 Lots of words to do with everyday chemistry begin with the word 'poly' such as polyester, polystyrene and polymer.

What is a 'polymer' and what does 'poly' mean when used in this way?

Find out what you can from the Internet and prepare a presentation for the rest of the class.

See pages 102–103 of your Student Book

Reactions running backwards

1 Design an eye-catching safety poster to display at a petrol station. Include the scientific reason for the instructions you are giving.

FIGURE 17: Why is it important to be safe at a petrol station?

2 Naked flames were always very dangerous in coal mines. Find out all you can about the Davy safety lamp. Who invented it? What did it look like and what were its important safety features?

Prepare an illustrated PowerPoint presentation to share what you find out with your class.

3 Set out below is the chemical reaction that takes place during photosynthesis.

water + carbon dioxide ➤ glucose + oxygen

What two things have to be present to make this reaction work?

Add them to the equation.

Now label the equation to show which substances are the reactants and which are the products.

Now look at the equation for respiration.

glucose + oxygen ➤ water + carbon dioxide

Label this equation to show which are the reactants and which are the products.

Look carefully at your two answers. What can you say about the reactants and the products in these two reactions?

Which of these reactions does a plant carry out during daylight hours?

Which reaction continues when it gets dark?

Types of energy

1 'All energy on the Earth comes originally from the Sun'.

Produce a PowerPoint presentation to explain this statement using any two of the following examples:

- the kinetic energy of a bicycle being ridden up a steep hill
- the electrical energy used to power a television set (hint – think about how the electricity might have been generated)
- the sound energy of a car engine as it moves along the road.

Test yourself 5-6

2 a Complete the table by giving one example of each type of energy.

Type of Energy	Example
Kinetic energy	
Chemical energy	
Electrical energy	
Heat (or thermal energy)	
Potential energy	
Gravitational energy	

b Where is nuclear energy stored?

c Where does the store of energy that you need come from?

d Find out the stored energy in 100 g of each of three different food items; remember to state the units as well as just the number!

Food 1 .... Energy per 100 g ....

Food 2 .... Energy per 100 g ....

Food 3 .... Energy per 100 g ....

Why is the stored energy always given for 100 g of each type of food?

Creative 7-8

3 Write an article for a magazine read by teenagers explaining why eating chocolate and crisps more than once everyday is not a good thing to do – but to enjoy chocolate and crisps occasionally is alright. Include some figures about energy values in your article.

Changing energy

Digital   HSW   3-4

1 Look at the illustration of the diver in question 2 on this page. Prepare a PowerPoint presentation showing each of the energy transfers that have taken place as the energy from the Sun is finally converted into the kinetic energy of this dive.

Test yourself   5-6

2 The drawings below show Caroline diving into a swimming pool.
As she falls, gravitational potential energy is changed into kinetic energy.

a Why does Caroline have **no** kinetic energy at A?

b The table shows Caroline's gravitational potential energy and kinetic energy at four stages of the dive.

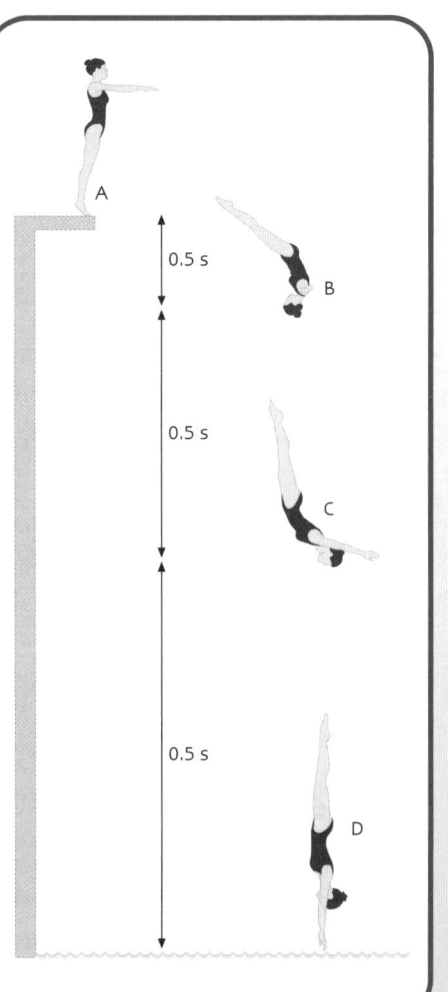

Stage of the dive	Total energy (kJ)	Gravitational potential energy (kJ)	Kinetic energy (kJ)
A	8	8	0
B	8	7	1
C	8	4	4
D	8	0	

i Write the missing kinetic energy value for stage D in the table.

ii As Caroline falls there is **no** loss of energy to the air.
How do the energy values for stages A, B, C and D show this?

Creative   7-8

3 As the cost of fuel gets higher, many families are trying to use less electricity at home. Write an information leaflet for teenagers that explains how they can help reduce the family's fuel bill without giving up any of their favourite activities.

Tracking energy transfers

1 Exercise always makes you hot!

Prepare a PowerPoint presentation to explain why running, cycling, playing football or dancing at a disco always makes a person feel hot.

Think about the useful and non-useful energy transfers that are taking place within the body.

FIGURE 1: When you cycle, how many energy transfers are there?

2 a Write a sentence describing the energy transfer for any **three** appliances in your home.

b Now draw an energy transfer diagram for each of those appliances.

c Now draw a Sankey diagram for each appliance – you will not know the actual figures but try to draw a sensible scale diagram showing how the energy is transferred. Don't forget the non-useful part of the transfer as well!

3 A large number of people now have energy efficient light bulbs in their homes.

Some other people are still not sure what the advantage of these bulbs is. Write an information leaflet explaining why energy efficient light bulbs are a good thing to use.

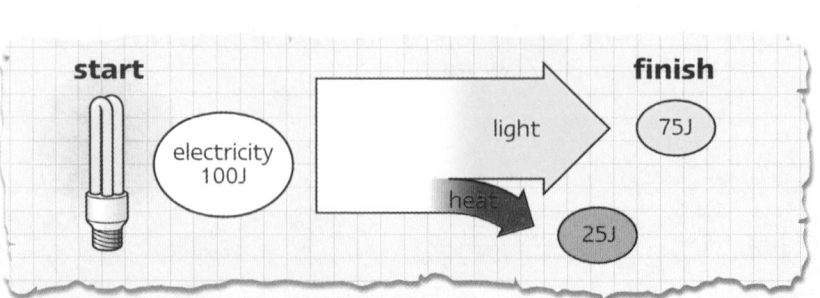

FIGURE 2: A Sankey diagram for an energy efficient light bulb.

What are fuels?

1 The drawings below show six ways of providing energy.

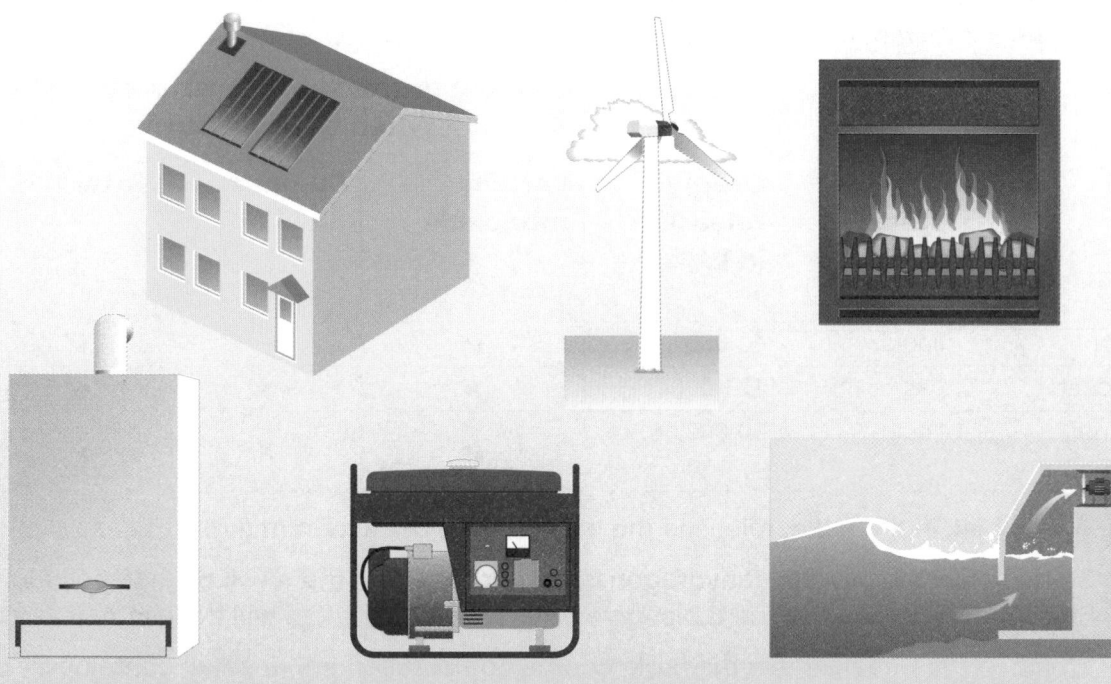

a From the drawings, give the names of **two** fossil fuels.

b What is the name of the chemical reaction that releases energy from fuels?

c Write an equation for this reaction.

2 Many people are concerned about the effect on the environment of burning fossil fuels. Write and draw a cartoon in which one person explains to another about the pollution caused by fossil fuels.

3 As fossil fuels will run out one day we need to look for alternatives. Your teacher will set up a wiki on the school intranet. Choose one alternative form of energy from the pictures in question 1 and find out **five** key facts that you can post on the site. When the whole class has done this you could ask another class to see if they could add to what you have written.

Energy release from fuels

1 The table below gives information about **three** fuels that can be used in cars.

✔ shows a substance is produced when the fuel burns.
✗ shows a substance is **not** produced when the fuel burns.

Fuel	Physical state	Energy released in kJ/kg	Some of the substances produced when the fuel burns		
			Carbon monoxide	Sulphur dioxide	Water
petrol	liquid	48 000	✔	✔	✔
hydrogen	gas	121 000	✗	✗	✔
ethanol (alcohol)	liquid	30 000	✔	✗	✔

a Which fuel, in the table, releases the least energy per kilogram (kg)?

b Some scientists say that if hydrogen is burned as a fuel there will be less pollution. From the information in the table, give **one** reason why there will be less pollution.

c Which of the three fuels in the table can be compressed into a small container?

d Which gas in the air is needed for fuels to burn?

carbon dioxide   nitrogen   oxygen   water vapour

e Petrol and ethanol are both fuels. Petrol is made from oil.
Scientists say that oil could run out in 100 years.
In some countries people plant sugar cane and use it to make ethanol.

Sugar cane will not run out. Explain why.

2 People in towns and cities all over the world are starting to use electric cars. Research these cars and produce a PowerPoint presentation with at least **three** advantages and **three** disadvantages of this type of car.

3 Imagine that you are designing a car in the year 2045. Design a brochure for your new car explaining all its good points. Most importantly of all, explain about the fuel that it uses and why it uses this kind of fuel.

ENERGY TRANSFER PROJECT

There is a great deal in the news about making our homes more energy efficient by preventing heat losses.

Design a model that you could use in a laboratory to investigate the effect of each of the following ways of insulating a home:

- loft insulation
- cavity wall insulation
- double glazing
- draft excluders.

When you have designed your model, carry out the following tasks.

1 Use your model to investigate how heat losses can be reduced by using each of these methods and combinations of them.

2 Evaluate how good your model has been and think of ways to improve it.

3 Research the cost of each method for a typical family home and write a report setting out the results of your experiment. In your report explain how this could help a family to save on their fuel bills, allowing for the cost of the energy efficiency measures.

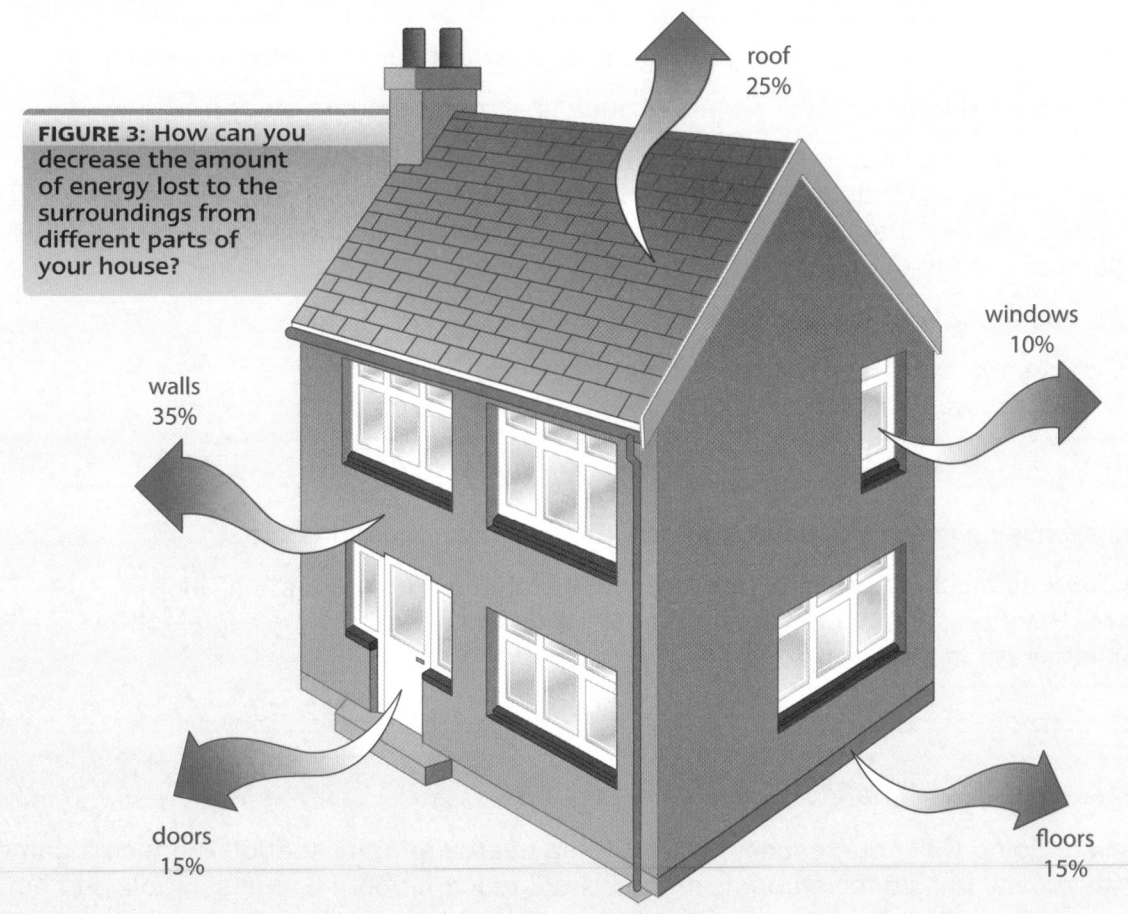

FIGURE 3: How can you decrease the amount of energy lost to the surroundings from different parts of your house?

roof 25%

windows 10%

walls 35%

doors 15%

floors 15%

Conductors and insulators

1 a Draw the circuit symbol for each of these components.
   i   lamp
   ii open switch
   iii closed switch
   iv voltmeter
   v   battery

b Copy the box below. Put a tick in the box to show if you think each of these items would complete an electric circuit and allow the current to flow.

Item tested	Completed circuit	Did not complete circuit
glass beaker		
aluminium toy car		
wooden spoon		
sheet of A4 paper		
stainless steel fork		

Describe an experiment that you could have carried out to get these results.

When asked to predict the results of such an experiment one student wrote:

'I think that the wooden spoon and the stainless steel fork will both complete the circuit as they will allow the current to flow in a straight line. The sheet of paper will be too thin and the beaker and the toy car are irregular shapes that current will not be able to pass through.'

Do you agree with this answer?

Can you explain why you think it is right or wrong?

2 It is always dangerous to have electrical appliances in the bathroom.

Find out as much as you can about why this statement is true and produce a PowerPoint presentation on safety that explains the dangers of having electrical appliances in the bathroom.

3 You are going with your teacher on a visit to a nearby primary school. Produce a game or an activity to help the students in the school to learn about circuit symbols and how to remember which is which.

See pages 124–125 of your Student Book

Current in circuits

3-4

Creative

1 Design a newspaper advertisement for some Christmas tree lights. The big selling point of these lights is that if one bulb breaks the others stay alight. Using what you know about circuits, explain how this happens in a way that will make people want to buy the lights.

5-6

Test yourself

2 **a** Max built **circuit 1** as shown.

He closed the switch, S, and all the bulbs came on. One of the bulbs then broke and **all** the bulbs went off.

Which bulb must have broken? Give the letter.

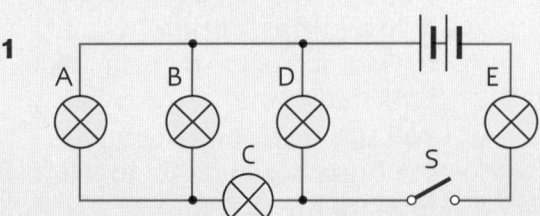

b Max built **circuit 2** as shown. He connected a plastic comb and a metal key in different parts of the circuit.

Look carefully at **circuit 2**. Copy and complete the table below to show which bulbs in circuit 2 will be on or off when different switches are open or closed. Write **on** or **off** in the boxes below.

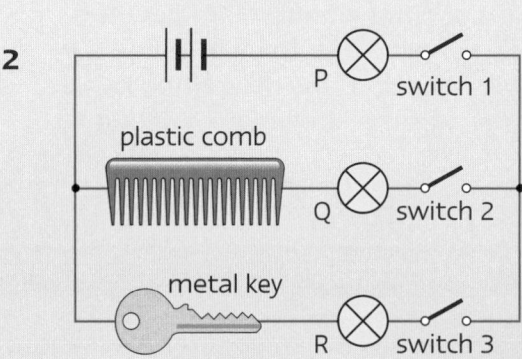

Switch 1	Switch 2	Bulb P	Bulb Q	Bulb R
open	open	off	off	off
open	closed			
closed	open			

Digital

HSW

7-8

3 Find out what resistance in an electrical circuit means; and be ready to give feedback in a class discussion in the next lesson.

Can you also find out what happens to the total resistance if two resistors are placed in series and then in parallel?

If all these resistors are the same, can you find out which circuit will have the greater resistance?

Energy in circuits

1 **a** Explain the difference between the voltage and current in a circuit.

b Choose the right word from each pair to complete this paragraph.

In a series circuit the **voltage/current** is always the same wherever you measure it. In a **series/parallel** circuit the voltage is the same in each branch and the **voltage/current** in each of the branches adds up to the total for the circuit.

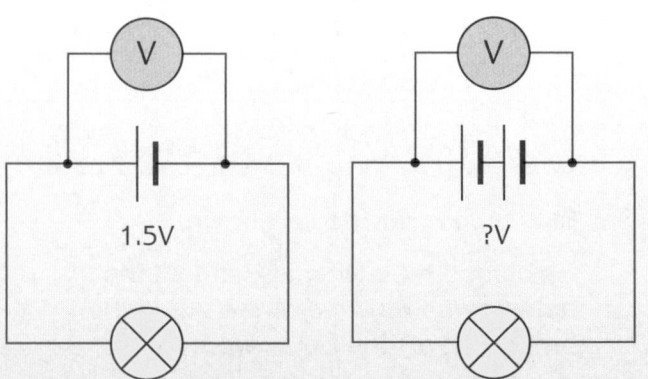

c What would you expect the value of V to be in circuit 2 if each of the cells is the same as the single cell in circuit 1?

2 The Volt is named after Alessandro Volta and the unit of current (the Amp) after Andre Ampere. Find out as much as you can about **one** of these two scientists and be prepared to give some feedback to the whole class in the next lesson. You could do this as a PowerPoint presentation or in any other form that you prefer.

Things you could include in your presentation:

- when they lived

- what country and town they lived in

- what was the experimental work that made them famous?

3 You have carried out a consumer survey by testing a number of batteries to see which one would allow a torch battery to remain alight for longest. Write a report on your survey but be sure to include a proper scientific explanation as to what is happening when a battery transfers energy to a light bulb.

Measuring the forces around you

1 **a** Complete the table to show the type of force needed for each activity.

Activity	Type of force
Moving a trolley around the supermarket	
Shutting a door	
Moving the pedals to ride a bicycle	
In a tug of war	
Holding a strong dog on a lead	
Using a spanner to tighten a nut	
Turning on a tap	

b Two teams are taking part in a tug of war and Team A pulls the rope with a force of 950 N.

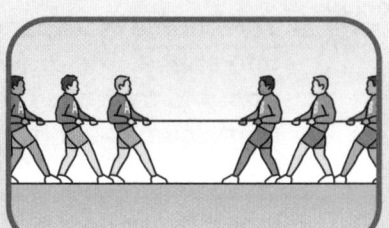

i Describe the size of the force that Team B would have to pull with in order to win the competition.

ii Draw a diagram of two teams in a tug of war. Label them Team A and Team B and then draw an arrow to show the direction of force that Team B would apply to the rope to win.

2 You might remember that when you were very young – in about Year 2 or Year 3 you first learnt about the idea of forces as pushes and pulls. Design an activity sheet that you could take on a visit to a primary school to help students of 6 or 7 years old begin to understand this idea. Make it colourful and easy to read and include lots of activities to try out at school and at home.

3 The Olympic Games are coming to London in the year 2012. Forces are very important in a lot of Olympic sports. Log on to the London 2012 website (www.london2012.com) and find out as much as you can about the forces involved in a sport of your choice. Put all the information about your chosen sport onto the wiki that your teacher will set up for you to share with everyone else's choice of sport.

Different forces around you

1 Draw a poster which describes the different kinds of contact forces.

2 Prepare a PowerPoint presentation on the rules that apply to contact forces. Give as many examples as you can and try and include some really good ways of remembering the rules.

3 **a** The shuttle is a spacecraft which is used to take satellites into space. The drawing opposite shows the shuttle just about to take off. The shuttle has a separate fuel tank containing liquid hydrogen and liquid oxygen.

Explain why hydrogen and oxygen are transported as liquids rather than as gases.

b The graph below shows how the upward force and the weight of the shuttle, including fuel, change during the first 20 seconds, after the fuel is ignited.

Why does the total weight of the shuttle **decrease** during the first 20 seconds?

c **i** Look at the graph. At 20 seconds, what is the value of:

the upward force on the shuttle?

the total weight of the shuttle and fuel?

ii At 20 seconds, what is the **resultant** force on the shuttle?

iii Use the graph to explain why the shuttle **cannot** take off before 10 seconds.

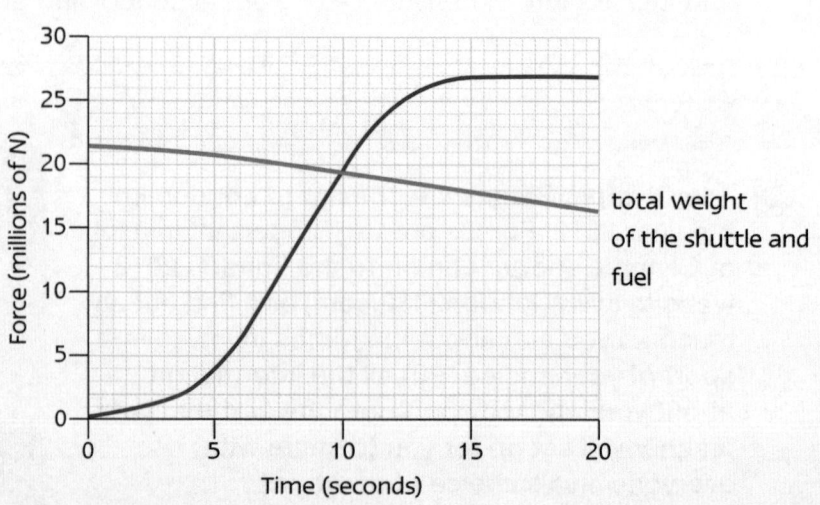

fuel tank

shuttle

total weight of the shuttle and fuel

Force (millions of N)

Time (seconds)

Balanced and unbalanced forces

1 Look at these drawings of cars and the arrows on them showing forces.

a Which one is accelerating?

b Why did you choose this one?

c Can you tell which one is standing still and which one is moving at a steady speed?

d Explain your answer to part **c**. Make sure that you write about balanced and unbalanced forces.

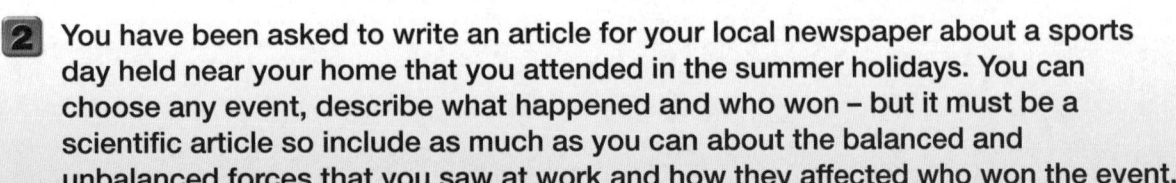

Creative

HSW

5-6

2 You have been asked to write an article for your local newspaper about a sports day held near your home that you attended in the summer holidays. You can choose any event, describe what happened and who won – but it must be a scientific article so include as much as you can about the balanced and unbalanced forces that you saw at work and how they affected who won the event.

Digital

7-8

3 Find out all that you can about Sir Isaac Newton and be ready to give a short presentation to the rest of the class.

The things you could research might include:

FIGURE 1: Sir Isaac Newton.

- when he lived

- where he was born

- what work he is remembered for

- what do apples and apple trees have to do with his scientific work

- what 'Newton's Laws' are?

- what did he invent that many of us have in our homes that we would not think of as very scientific? (this is quite a hard one – but see if you can find out)

Speeding along

Test yourself 3–4

1 **a** What does the term ‘constant speed’ mean?

b What does the term ‘average speed’ mean?

c Copy and complete the table showing the average speeds for some journeys.

Time taken	Distance travelled	Average speed
1 hour	25 kilometres	
10 seconds	100 metres	
1 hour		15 km/h
	50 kilometres	25 km/h
3 hours	75 kilometres	

d Which of these would be the speed of an Olympic sprinter?

Creative 5–6

2 Look at the information in the table on page 143 of the Student Book. Present this information in another form that makes it easy to understand and remember.

Digital 7–8

3 There have been a lot of attempts at the world land speed record. Find out all you can about either the current holder of this record or someone who has held the record or tried to break the record in the past. Add what you find into the wiki that your teacher will set up so that between the whole class you produce the history of land speed record attempts.

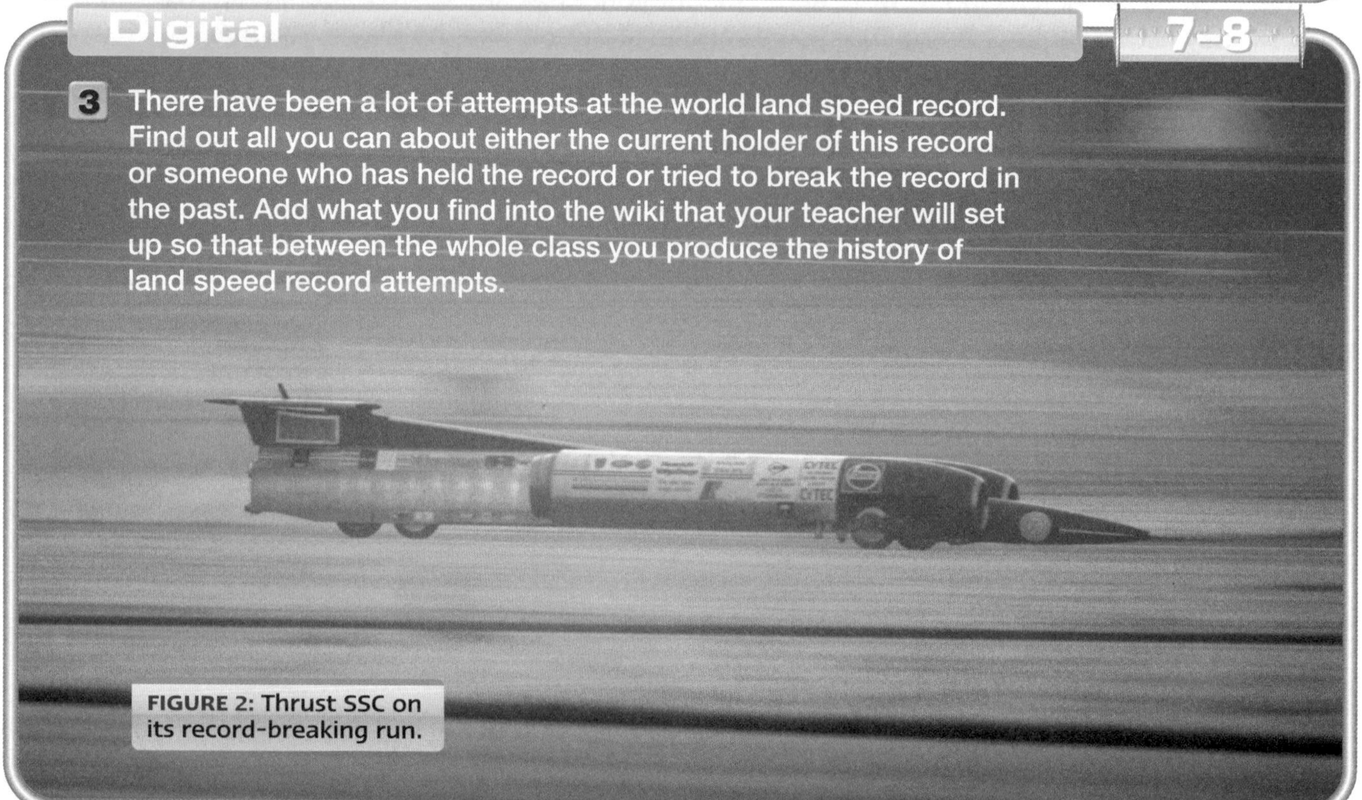

FIGURE 2: Thrust SSC on its record-breaking run.

See pages 142–143 of your Student Book

Different types of road have different speed limits. There are often speed cameras to make sure that drivers do not go too fast.

Find a speed camera near to your home or school.

What is the speed limit on that stretch of road?

Why do you think a speed camera has been placed in that position?

Do you think that more speed limit signs are better than more speed cameras?

What can you find out about how speed cameras work – can you explain the science behind how they measure speed?

You may also want to look at the popularity of speed cameras amongst drivers. Do they think speed cameras are a good idea or a bad idea?

Once you have gathered all of your information, create an advertising campaign to explain the benefits of speed cameras to drivers. You may want to focus on how many road accidents they help to prevent and also the benefits to your local community. Your campaign can be on paper, on computer or in the form of a podcast.

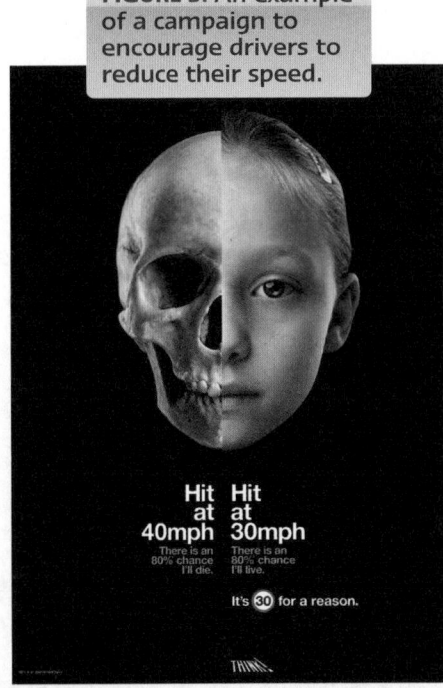

FIGURE 3: An example of a campaign to encourage drivers to reduce their speed.

FIGURE 4: How popular are speed cameras?

Measuring the speed

1
  a What is meant by the term SI unit?

  b Why is it important to have SI units?

  c What are the SI units of:

    i time

    ii distance.

  d Choose the measuring instrument that you would use to measure each of these distances.

    30 cm ruler   tape measure   car milometer   metre ruler

    i The distance between London and Edinburgh.

    ii The length of the corridor outside your school science lab.

    iii The size of an exercise book.

    iv The size of the bench or table you work at in science lessons.

2 A long car journey might be completed at an average speed of 70 kilometres per hour; but this might include stretches on a motorway, in a town, stopping at traffic lights and roundabouts and even being stuck in a traffic jam. Can you think of an interesting way to show the different stages in such a journey, and the speed at which the car is travelling at each stage?

3 Can you design a measuring device that can measure exactly 1 minute? You cannot use batteries or electricity; and you can only use materials that you would normally find at home or at school.

Prepare a presentation showing how your device would be made and what you think the strengths and weaknesses of your design would be.

As well as accuracy you should think about things like cost, how easy it is to make and whether you could use it on more than one occasion.

Friction

1 Draw a poster or a cartoon strip explaining how friction slows you down on a slide – and what you can do to make yourself go faster!

Test yourself 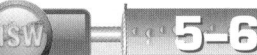 5-6

2 a Where on a car do we rely on friction to help us to drive safely? Give **three** examples.

   b For one of the examples you have given describe a situation where the friction might be reduced and explain why this might make driving the car more difficult or less safe.

   c In countries where the winters are very snowy drivers often put chains on the tyres of their cars. Can you suggest what these snow chains do – and why it would be important to take them off when the snow thawed?

FIGURE 5: Can you think why snow chains are important in countries with harsh winters?

Digital 7-8

3 Friction wears away moving parts and reduces the efficiency of moving objects such as trains on rails.

   Could you design a way of reducing the friction between a train and the railway line that would make the train move more quickly and use less fuel?

   Use the Internet to research the ideas that have been tried in various parts of the world and be ready to present your ideas in the next lesson.

Air resistance

3–4

Digital

1 Prepare a PowerPoint presentation to describe how the air resistance changes if you start off walking slowly, and then walk faster and then start to run.

On your final slide answer this question: 'Why does air resistance mean that there is a maximum speed at which you can run?'

5–6

Creative

2 Draw a poster to explain how the air resistance of a car or lorry or train or a racing bicycle and its rider can be reduced. Make sure you explain what happens to the particles in the air and how the design of the vehicle can help to reduce this.

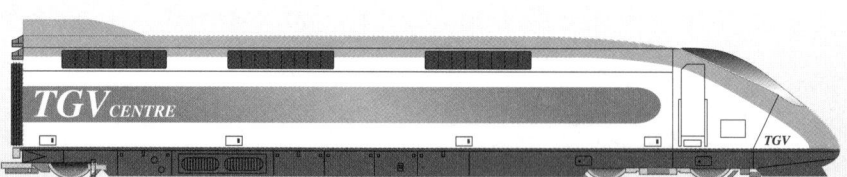

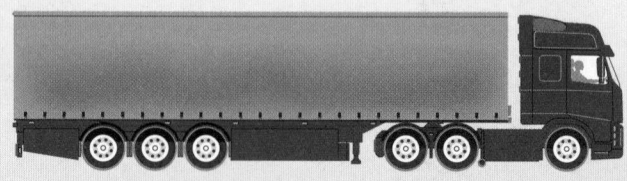

Test yourself

HSW **7–8**

3 a i Draw a graph of the speed of a skydiver against the time from jumping from the aeroplane to reaching the ground.

ii Mark on your graph the points at which terminal velocity is reached.

iii On the same axes sketch a second graph for a skydiver with a parachute that has twice the surface area of the first.

b Think of a diver diving from a high board through the air and into the water. Can you describe how the forces on the diver change and what happens to their speed as a result?

Streamlining and drag

1 **a** What **two** effects can a more streamlined design have on a vehicle?
Copy the table and tick the correct boxes.

It can make it easier to park a car in tight spaces.	
It can increase the top speed.	
It can make it easier to drive around sharp bends and corners.	
It means a vehicle can travel further on the same amount of fuel.	
It can make a car more stable.	
It makes it easier to get a good paint finish.	

b Describe what happens to the particles in the air if a car has a more smoothed–out shape.

c Can you name an animal that has a streamlined shape to enable it to run faster?

2 Prepare an information leaflet explaining why boats are shaped as they are which you could take with you on a visit to a primary school with your teacher. Make it colourful and interesting to look at – but remember that it is the science that is really important.

3 To win a cycle race the riders must make sure that they and their bikes are as streamlined as they can be. Find out all you can about how the design of racing bikes and clothing has changed over the years to bring this about. The Tour de France website (www.letour.fr) would be a good place to start – but you will have to look in other places too. Prepare a presentation in any form you choose on this topic. Think about using pictures and video clips if you can find them on sites that are free to download – otherwise use your own pictures and diagrams. Remember as always to use as much scientific knowledge in your presentation as you possibly can.

How do we classify?

1 Copy and complete this table by listing the five vertebrate groups and giving one key feature for each group.

Vertebrate group	One key feature
Fish	
	Eggs with brittle shells
Mammals	
	Moist skin
	Tough leathery eggs

Look at the photo of the rhinoceros beetle on page 161 of your Student Book.

Which of the vertebrate groups does this creature belong in?

Explain your answer.

Creative 5-6

2 Create a mind map to help you learn the different groups of the vertebrates. You will need to include the name, features and examples of each group. There is a lot of scope in this task to use colour and simple illustrations. Start at the centre of a blank landscape piece of paper, with a colourful image to represent the subject.

Digital 7-8

3 The system we use for classifying organisms was invented by Carl Linnaeus. Do some Internet/book research on Carl Linnaeus and prepare a PowerPoint presentation suitable to show to the rest of your class.

Include information such as:

- where and when he was born
- the origin of his surname
- what he spent a lot of his life doing
- what his famous book on plant classification was called.

Linnaeus used and therefore promoted the binomial system of classification – explain simply what this means.

What are humans called using this system?

See pages 160–161 of your Student Book

The five kingdoms

Digital   3-4

1 Remembering the five groups in the plant kingdom is not easy.

Carry out some research and find some good pictures of plants from the five different groups. A helpful website to look at is www.perspective.com/nature/plantae/.

You may want to look at:

- how do they reproduce?
- what conditions do they prefer?
- what are the main features of the plants?

Use this information to produce five pocket-sized fact cards, one for each plant group. Use pieces of card no bigger than standard postcards and make each fact both attractive and informative.

Creative   5-6

2 Using drawings more than words, design an information poster that shows clearly the differences between the four groups of arthropods. Although the basic details of these differences are covered in your Student Book (page 162) you may need to use other books or maybe the Internet to find some examples of each arthropod.

You want lots of people to read your poster so make sure that it's bright and packed full of fascinating facts.

Test yourself   7-8

3 Copy and complete this table to show evidence both for and against fungi, protists and bacteria being originally classified as plants.

Organism	Possible evidence for	Possible evidence against
Fungi		
Protists		
Bacteria		

One student, when answering a question like this, thought that chlorophyll must appear somewhere in the table. Explain as clearly as you can the connection between chlorophyll and plants.

Water for plants

Digital  3-4

1 Carry out some Internet research into desert plants and be prepared to make a presentation to the rest of the class.

You should try to find out information such as:

- the names of some types of desert plants (with pictures if possible)
- the kinds of conditions they have to survive in
- the special ways that they are adapted to these conditions.

Creative 5-6

2 You have been asked to make transpiration easy to understand for Year 6 students. Design a poster that explains about the best and worst conditions for this process.

Apart from being attractive and accurate your poster **must** compare transpiration with the everyday activity of drying washing (on a line that is, not in a tumble dryer!). This simple analogy should help your explanation.

Test yourself  7-8

3 Mango trees are grown in hot, dry countries where soil can be hard and tightly compacted. To water the trees farmers spray water on to the soil around the trees.

Look at this drawing, which shows a new way of watering mango trees.

Use the information in the introduction and the diagram to write a clear explanation of why this is a much more reliable method of getting water to mangos and why it results in a 15% increase in fruit production.

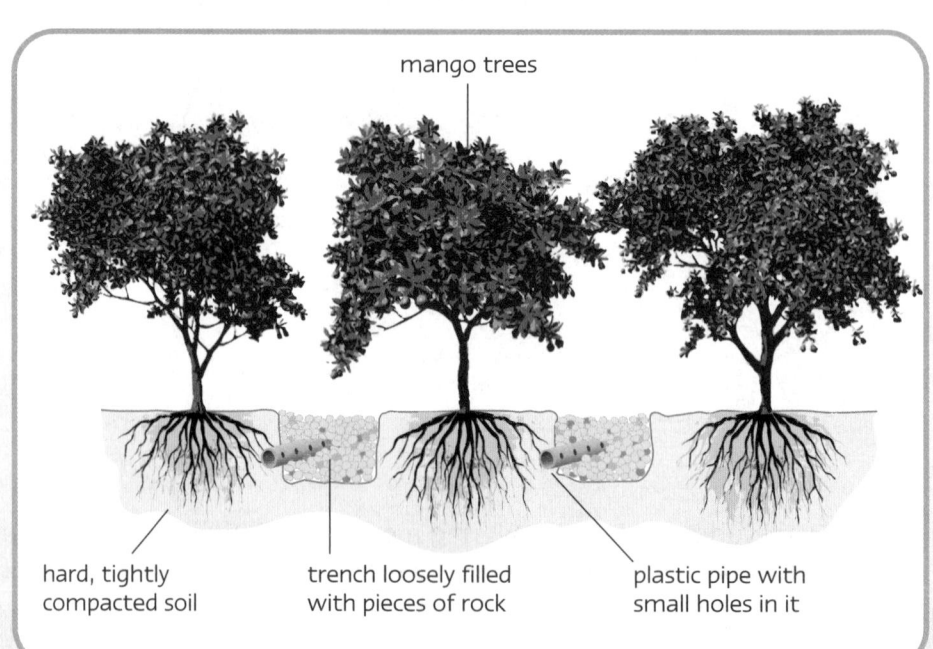

mango trees

hard, tightly compacted soil

trench loosely filled with pieces of rock

plastic pipe with small holes in it

See pages 164–165 of your Student Book

Why do we need plants?

1 Cacti, conifers and marram grass have leaves that are specially adapted for dry climates. Do some Internet or book research on the leaves of these three plants.

Use this information to produce a short presentation for the rest of the class.

You could produce a PowerPoint presentation or alternatively produce a display that you are able to talk about when making your presentation.

Try to bring in any examples of these leaves to show your class.

Test yourself 5-6

2 Sketch this diagram showing a slice of leaf as seen under a microscope.

On the diagram use letters to indicate:

a which part prevents excessive water loss

b where gases enter and leave

c which type of cell carries out most photosynthesis.

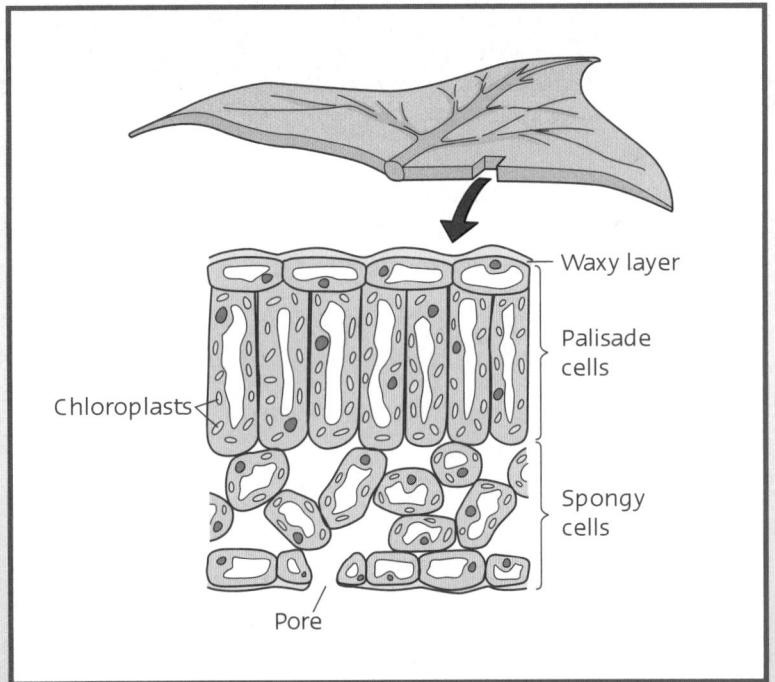

Creative 7-8

3 Use the information from pages 164–167 of your Student Book to produce a poster describing movement of water from the soil to the air through a plant. You must show and name all the key structures, indicate what drives the flow of water through the plant and show what the water is used for.

Intelligent use of diagrams, labels and symbols means that there should be relatively few words, i.e. don't write any explanations that go beyond one or two short sentences.

CLASSIFICATION AND FOOD WEBS PROJECT

FIGURE 1: Organic farming in California.

On page 168 of your Student Book Mary is trying to look after her plants organically. This means without using chemicals to kill pests. It also means without using fertilisers on her plants.

Carry out some research into organic gardening/farming. Try to find out all the advantages and disadvantages compared to using chemicals.

There are lots of points to consider e.g.

- money
- health risks
- damage to other wildlife
- amount of crop that can be produced
- people's jobs (if you look at it from the point of view of farming).

Gather as much information as you can from a number of sources and make sure you have some opinions for and against.

Back in class, working as a group, you are going to prepare a presentation that argues for or against organic gardening/farming.

Your group will first of all have to agree which position you are going to take and then prepare a persuasive argument for this position.

To accompany your presentation it would be a good idea to produce a large colourful campaign poster and maybe design some badges and a slogan.

See page 168 of your Student Book

Are leaves bigger in the shade?

1 In a SAT question a student was asked to describe where plants get water from and she wrote:

From the rain.

This is not entirely wrong but it is not a full answer. Write a more accurate answer to this question.

The next part of the question asked why leaves have a waxy upper layer and the student wrote:

To stop the leaves soaking up water.

This is completely incorrect. Write the correct answer.

Now explain why the student's original answer was wrong.

2 Imagine you are the nature correspondent for the school magazine. Write a short article about the differences in woodland in early spring compared to mid-summer. Your article must focus on things such as the availability of light at ground level, the presence and appearance of flowering plants on the woodland floor; soil conditions etc. and you must offer explanations for the differences you describe.

3 Read again the 'Size of leaves' investigation on page 171 of your Student Book. To make this investigation more scientific we could calculate the surface area of the leaves rather than measuring their size.

Carry out some research and firstly find and write down a clear explanation of what we mean when we use the term 'surface area'.

Then find out (or think of yourself) a suitable method for working out the surface area of a leaf. Describe your method clearly and then test it out by collecting a leaf and working out its area.

If you have time you could repeat the investigation from page 171 using your method.

See pages 170–171 of your Student Book

What conditions do animals prefer?

1 A group of students carried out the investigation on page 173 of your Student Book. Here are their results:

	30 seconds	60 seconds	90 seconds	120 seconds	150 seconds
No. of woodlice in the light	5	3	2	1	
No. of woodlice in the dark	5	7	8	9	

a Copy and complete the table with your estimate of the numbers in light and dark after 150 seconds.

b Explain why you have chosen the numbers you have added to the table.

c Looking at figures in a table does not always show patterns as clearly as other types of chart. Use the figures in the table to draw a bar chart and add colour to the bars. (Hint: put time along the bottom of the chart and number of woodlice up the side.)

d Suggest why woodlice seem to prefer dark conditions.

2 Carry out some research on woodlice. Try to find out information on:

- the full range of conditions they prefer (not just light and dark)
- what they eat
- how their bodies are adapted for survival
- where they fit into the classification system you studied earlier in this topic
- any other interesting information you can find.

Now turn this information into a PowerPoint presentation called 'The world of woodlice'.

3 This question asks you to put your investigation design skills to the test. With the aid of clear diagrams and step-by-step instructions show how you would adapt the investigation on page 173 to:

a see if woodlice prefer damp or dry conditions, and

b see if woodlice prefer smooth or rough surfaces.

The challenge here is finding a way to recreate these conditions using a choice chamber. Don't forget to make each investigation a fair and valid test i.e. only vary one condition at a time and use a suitable sample size.

How plants and animals survive

1 Look at this photo of penguins in what is called a huddle.

This is behaviour that helps them survive in the harsh winter weather in Antarctica.

The penguins continually change position from the inside to the outside of the huddle.

Explain how this behaviour will help them to survive.

Explain why behaving like this could put the penguins in danger from predators.

2 The survival of animals does not just depend on their special features; it also depends on their behaviour.

Two of the most common types of survival behaviour are migration and hibernation. Carry out some research on these two behaviours and be prepared to give a presentation to your group. Try to give a number of examples of animals in each group. If you type in animal migration to www.youtube.co.uk you will see some wonderful examples of how different animals migrate.

3 Your friend is struggling to understand the idea of biodiversity so you decide to help by producing a couple of illustrated fact sheets.

Your task is to produce one fact sheet that explains what high biodiversity means and one that explains what low biodiversity means.

Each sheet should focus on one appropriate area, show the kinds of plants and animals present and explain the reasons for it being high or low. (Hint: think about the harshness of the conditions.)

Make sure the fact sheets are attractive as well as informative.

Food chains and webs

1 Look at these drawings of woodland animals:

Use these organisms to write out a food chain containing **three** links.

Write down which organism is the producer.

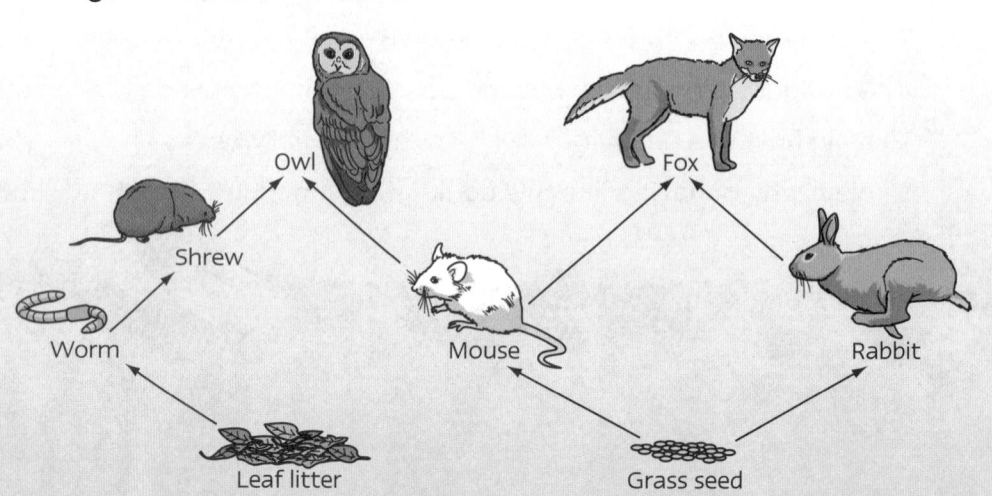

2 This question involves you in both research and communication.
From page 181 of your Student Book read about the 1952 myxomatosis epidemic. Use the information in this piece to prepare a PowerPoint presentation that will inform your classmates about the following aspects of the epidemic.

a The organisms that were affected by the epidemic and the feeding relationships between them. (Hint: you could produce a food web to show the organisms involved.)

b How the numbers of grass plants, rabbits and buzzards compared with each other both before and after the epidemic. (Hint: you could show this information using pyramids of numbers.)

As an alternative to a PowerPoint, you could present this information in the form of simple models!

3 Pyramids of numbers are not always a traditional pyramid shape (i.e. wide at the bottom and narrow at the top).

Design a poster that features all of the different pyramid shapes you have learned about. Your poster needs to include a simple explanation of why each pyramid is the shape it is. Your poster should be colourful, easy to read and informative – like the kind of posters you see in your classrooms.

See pages 176–177 of your Student Book

Looking at rocks

Test yourself HSW 3–4

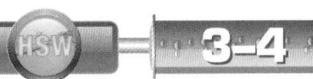

1 Copy the words and phrases below and then draw lines on the diagram to link up each rock type with its correct properties and a correct example.

Rock type	Properties	Example
Igneous	Changed by heat and pressure from earlier rocks	Limestone
Sedimentary	Crystalline, very hard	Marble
Metamorphic	Quite soft, formed in layers	Granite

Creative HSW 5–6

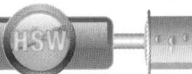

2 Create a mind map on the structure and properties of rocks.
Start at the centre of a blank landscape piece of paper, with a colourful image to represent the subject (remember – a picture is worth a thousand words!).
Thinking ahead to the next section you might want to include possible uses of the different types of rock.

Remember - mind maps should be colourful and attractive to encourage people to look at them.

Digital 7–8

3 Look at this photo of a crumbling section of Britain's coastline.

Do some Internet research (the BBC News website is a good source) and write a newspaper article about coastal erosion in the UK. You could focus on a specific area, like the White Cliffs of Dover. Add pictures and quotes just like a real article and also make sure there is some science in there too.

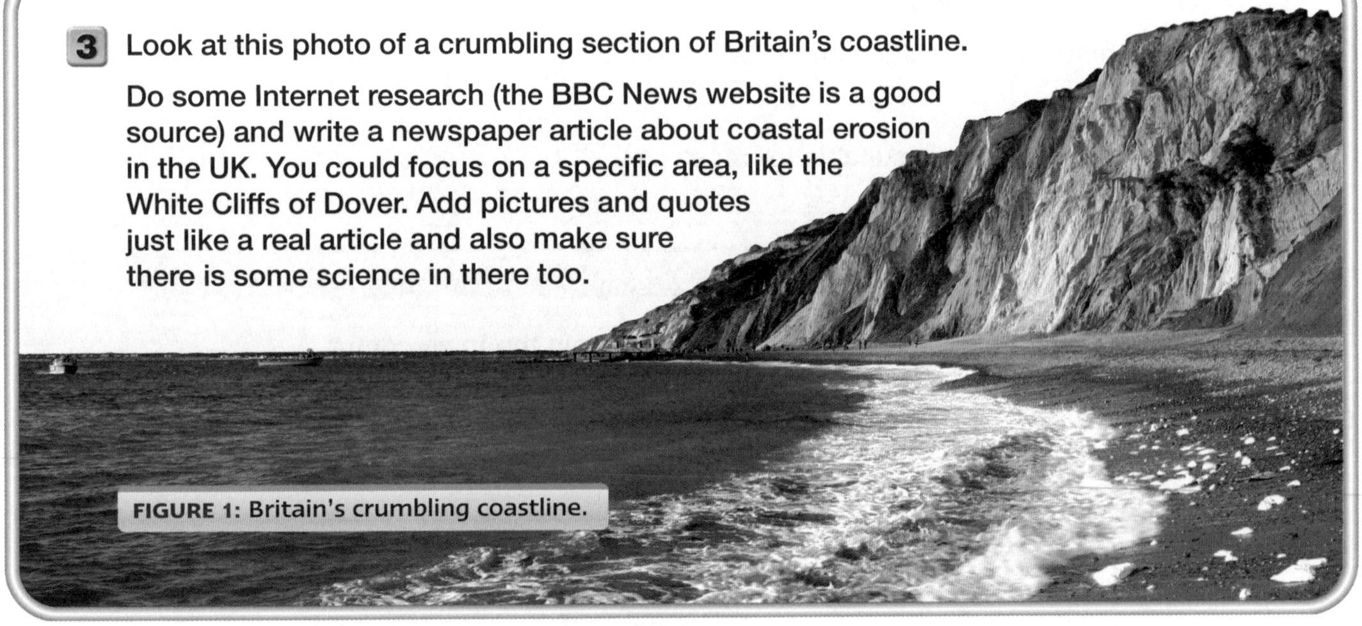

FIGURE 1: Britain's crumbling coastline.

See pages 184–185 of your Student Book

Using rocks

1 Look at this photograph of a First World War cemetery in France.

These headstones were put up in 1920.

Use this information and page 186 in your Student Book to answer these questions:

a How old is the cross in the photo?

b How would you describe its condition?

c Explain why this type of stone was chosen for the thousands of First World War graves.

d Give **one** reason why sandstone was not chosen for the crosses.

FIGURE 2: What kind of stone was used for these headstones?

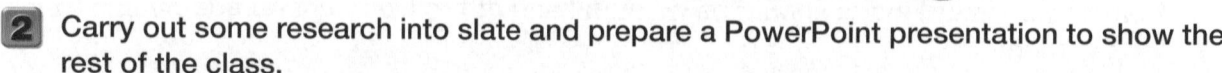

2 Carry out some research into slate and prepare a PowerPoint presentation to show the rest of the class.

The kind of information you need to research includes:

- how it is formed.
- where it can be found.
- something about the slate industry.
- its features.
- its uses (and why it is suitable for these uses).

3 The local council is considering building a statue in the town centre. You are an expert in rocks and you have been asked for your advice on what rock to use. You realise that before you can suggest a rock type you need a lot more information.

Write a letter to the council asking all the questions you need answers to before you can make a decision.

See pages 186–187 of your Student Book

Weathering of rocks

Test yourself
3–4

1 Against each of these statements about weathering of rocks write T if it is true or F if it is false.

a Animals and plants can cause weathering of rock.

b Marble is a rock that weathers very easily.

c Rocks can be broken up by ice.

d Water can only weather rocks when it freezes.

e Glaciers are fast-moving rivers of ice.

f Underground caves can be made by the weathering of rock.

Creative
5–6

2 Produce a poster that summarises all the different types of weathering. Use lots of illustrations rather than lots of words and make sure that you include real examples. (Hint: Look at page 189 in your Student Book.)
Remember this is an educational poster and it must therefore be attractive and informative.

Digital
7–8

3 Carry out some research into the daily temperature range (highest and lowest temperatures) in the winter at the North Pole, Death Valley in California and Northern England.

Use this information and your knowledge of freeze-thaw weathering to explain in which of the three areas you are more likely to find examples of rocks weathered in this way. Explain your reasoning as clearly as possible.

FIGURE 3: There is a great difference in temperature between the North Pole and Death Valley.

Pebble and powder science

1 Write out the following passage about the wearing away of rocks choosing words from the following list to complete the passage. You may use each word once, more than once or not at all.

rounded   wind   water   sharp   clue   bumps   hard   always

Sand is a .... material. Grains of sand are moved around by the .... Desert sand dunes are .... moving. When one sand grain .... into another one, its .... corners are worn away. This means that sand grains from a desert are .... This effect gives you a .... as to where a piece of sandstone might have come from.

2 As mentioned on page 190 of your Student Book most beaches are made up of a mineral called quartz.

Carry out some Internet research on this mineral and sand generally and be prepared to make a short presentation about it to your class.

Things you might want to find out include:

- its appearance under a microscope
- its uses (other than for lying on)
- types of sand
- is there a link with wrist watches?

3 This is a practical activity that should be easy to complete at home. You will need a jam jar or a one litre plastic bottle and some clean sand.

Add enough sand to half fill the container and then top up with clean water. Put the lid on the container and swirl it so that the water and sand is fully mixed. Now leave the container for five minutes and then complete the following tasks.

a Describe (with the aid of a diagram) the appearance of the contents after five minutes.

b Explain your observations.

c Predict what would happen if as well as sand you had small bits of gravel in the container (use a diagram if necessary).

d Explain your prediction.

e Use your observations to explain why sandy beaches do not build up at the side of fast flowing rivers.

See pages 190–191 of your Student Book

Rapid weathering

Test yourself 3–4

1 Write out the following sentences choosing the words below to help you complete the sentences.
The words may be used once, more than once or not all.

bigger **slow** **easier** **smooth** **more** **rounded** **faster** **weather**

a Weathering is a very .... process.

b Small pieces of rock .... more quickly than large pieces.

c Breaking a piece of rock reveals .... surfaces.

d Small pieces of rock are also .... to move.

e Pebbles are often .... and ....

f The .... the surface area the .... the weathering.

Creative HSW 5–6

2 Your friend is struggling to understand the idea of surface area and the weathering of rocks. You know that if a large rock splits into smaller pieces then there are lots more surfaces that can be attacked by the weather. This makes further weathering faster. To help your friend, use plasticine or cardboard or any other suitable material to make a simple series of models that show this principle.

Digital 7–8

3 Sandstone cliffs are very vulnerable to weathering and large chunks regularly fall away in winter. You are an expert called in by the government to advise on protecting the coastline.

Carry out some research into ways of protecting the coastline and then write a report giving suggestions as to what can be done. Make sure that you give a full explanation as to how your suggestions work.

FIGURE 4: How would you protect this coastline?

See pages 192–193 of your Student Book

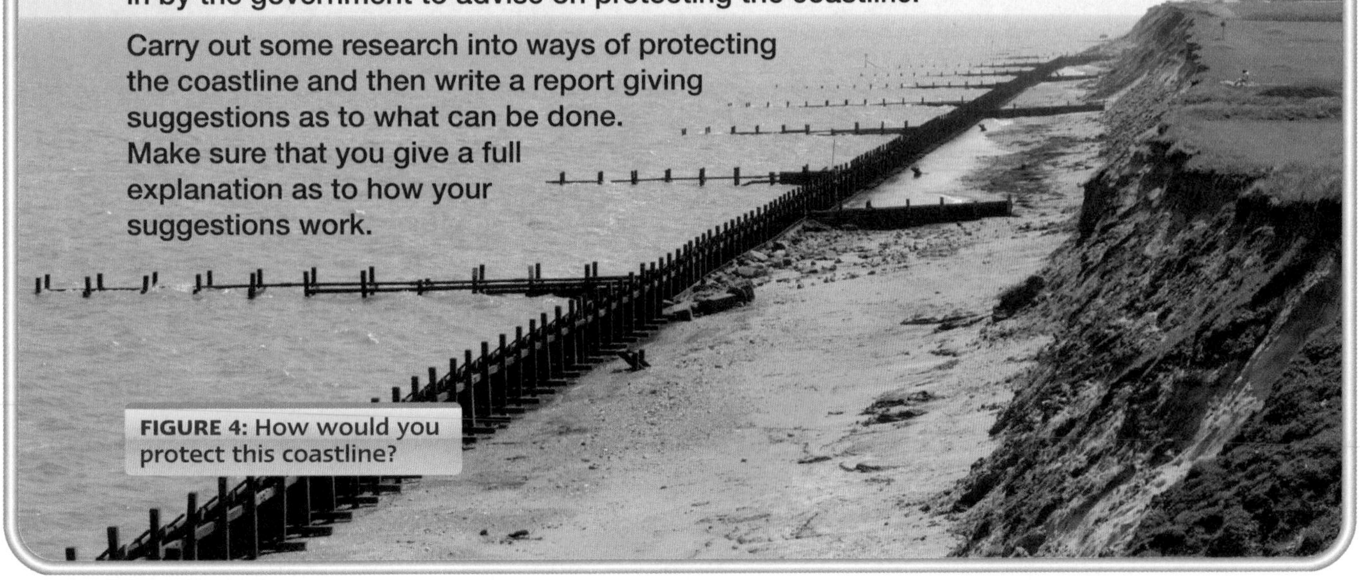

WEATHERING AND FOSSILS PROJECT

It's not only famous statues that get a clean-up.

Look at this photo of a workman sand blasting a building.

This has been a common occurrence in Britain in recent years.

In this project you are going to research the buildings in your local area, not the relatively modern houses made of brick but the older stone buildings.

As you walk around town take photographs of each building (if possible) and record your observations on a sheet like this:

FIGURE 5: A sandblaster at work

Name of building e.g. Town Hall (or name of company e.g. Lloyds Bank)	Type of stone e.g. sandstone, marble, granite, limestone	Age (it might say on it or members of your family might help here)	Clean or dirty

As well as this practical research you also need to use the Internet or the library to find out about the types of industry that were once present in your area so that you can link this to possible pollution damage to buildings.

Also try to research into the typical kind of stone found underground in your general area. Is there any link with the stone used for the buildings?

Back in class you are going to add your research to everybody else's findings to create a display about the history and use of stone in your area.

The aim will be to bring the study of rocks alive by linking it to where you live!

See page 194 of your Student Book

Transporting rocks

1 This question is designed to test some of your knowledge so far on this topic. Copy and complete this table with information about rocks and then check your answers using pages 184–196 in your Student Book.

Rock type	Example	One property	One use	Easily weathered?
Igneous			Road building	
	Limestone			
Metamorphic		Hard		No

2 You are out walking with your family by a slow-flowing river and you notice a boat called a dredger. The dredger is scooping up lots of sediment from the river and carrying it away. Look at the photograph of this boat and then write an article for the school magazine that explains:

a What the boat is doing.

b Why it is necessary.

Don't forget to use the science you have learned to help in your article.

FIGURE 6: A dredger at work.

3 Look at the photograph of the winding river on page 196 of your Student Book. Carry out some research into slow-moving rivers and prepare a short presentation to the class to explain why it is not just flowing in a straight line.

Rocks and heat

1 Copy the words and phrases below and then use straight lines to link up each original rock with its correct new metamorphic rock and the correct cause of the change.

Original rock	New metamorphic rock	Cause
Sandstone	Marble	Pressure
Mudstone	Quartzite	Heat
Limestone	Slate	Heat

2 The hardest natural material is diamond and this is formed as a result of metamorphism.

Carry out some research into diamonds and their formation and produce a PowerPoint presentation using your information.

The kind of information you find out might include:

- exactly how they are formed
- where in the world they can be found
- what are their uses
- why they are so expensive.

3 Baking has some similarities to the formation of metamorphic rocks.

Your friend is struggling to understand what happens when metamorphic rocks are formed. Use the model of baking to help explain the process. For scientific accuracy it would be useful to point out the differences as well as the similarities.

FIGURE 7: How is the formation of metamorphic rock similar to baking?

Fossil past

1 Copy and complete the following passage choosing words from this list. You may use each word once, more than once or not at all.

cliffs   preserved   rock   amber   sedimentary   tar   igneous

Fossils are the .... remains of plants and animals.

Fossils are usually made of .... The only type of rock in

which fossils can be found is .... rock.

The preserved bodies of animals can also be found in materials like ....

and .... A good place to find fossils is in .... at the seaside.

2 Use the information on pages 200 and 201 of your Student Book to produce a storyboard of how shell creatures (such as ammonites) from millions of years ago eventually ended up as fossils that were discovered by man.

Use a side of plain A4 paper for each section of the storyboard and try to use clear drawings supported by key words. Be prepared to talk the rest of the class through your storyboard when it is finished.

FIGURE 8: Ammonite fossils.

3 Fossils are the remains of plants and animals that have been preserved in rocks. There are however lots of examples of animals that have been preserved for many thousands of years in materials like amber, tar and ice.

Carry out some research into the preservation of animals by these methods and prepare a PowerPoint presentation.

You should include information like:

- examples (with pictures if possible) of animals preserved in different ways

- how these methods work

- what the key difference is between these methods and fossilisation.

How fossil fuels are made

1 Design an information poster to encourage members of the public to use less fossil fuel. You need to tell the public two key things:

- why they must do this,
- how they might go about it.

Make the poster attractive as well as informative.

2 True or false?
Against each of these statements about fossil fuels put a T for true or an F for false.

a All fossil fuels are made from plants.

b Fossil fuels are formed over millions of years.

c Fossil fuels are non-renewable energy sources.

d Coal and oil are both extracted from mines.

e Natural gas is usually found together with oil.

f Coal is likely to be the first fossil fuel to run out.

g Burning fossil fuels does not cause pollution.

h High pressure and heat were involved in making fossil fuels.

3 You know that fossil fuels are often found deep underground. Carry out some research into the dangers of coal mining and drilling for oil. Use this information to produce a PowerPoint presentation which explains why coal mining in particular is considered one of the world's most dangerous jobs.

It would be useful to find out about some real disasters associated with these jobs e.g. the Piper Alpha oil rig explosion.

In your presentation be as scientifically detailed as you can about the dangers.

FIGURE 9: An oil rig at sea.

Finding fossil fuels

1 Carry out some research to find out all the different uses to which oil is put. Don't just concentrate on oil as a fuel but find out about all the things that are made from oil. Use this information to produce a PowerPoint presentation entitled 'Our life without oil'. In your presentation you will explain how different our life might be when all the oil has run out. You can use examples of all the modern gadgets and materials that we won't have (or will have to replace with alternatives). One idea would be to show how different a typical day for you or your friends might be.

Test yourself 5-6

2 A big use of fossil fuels is in making electricity.
This table shows the percentage of electricity generated using coal, oil and gas over a 25-year period in the UK.

	1980	1990	2000	2005
Coal	72	67	31	33
Oil	13	8	2	1
Gas	1	1	39	39

a Draw a bar chart to show the pattern in this data.

b Since 1980 which fuel have we used more of to produce electricity?

c Why do you think oil usage has fallen to only 1%?

d Which fuel used to make electricity in the UK is not mentioned here?

e Give a reason why this fuel has not been mentioned in this section of your Student Book.

Creative 7-8

3 Britain used to produce enough oil from the North Sea to meet its own needs and to be able to sell oil abroad. Unfortunately North Sea oil no longer covers all our needs.

Look at the map on page 204 of your Student Book. Use this information to write a short explanation of why oil is becoming more and more expensive in Britain and why we are getting more worried about our supplies. Some things to think about might be:

- distances that the oil must travel to reach us,
- friendly and unfriendly countries.

Notes

Notes

Acknowledgements

The Publishers gratefully acknowledge the following for permission to reproduce copyright material. Whilst every effort has been made to trace the copyright holders, in cases where this has been unsuccessful or if any have inadvertently been overlooked, the Publishers will be pleased to make the necessary arrangements at the first opportunity.

The Publishers would like to thank the following for permission to reproduce photographs:

p. 10 © AP / PA Photos; p. 10 © John Watney / Science Photo Library; p. 12 © Michelle Del Guercio, Peter Arnold Inc. / Science Photo Library; p. 29 © iStockphoto.com / Sebastian Kaulitzki; p. 14 © Free Agents Limited / Corbis; p. 16 © Bettmann / Corbis; p. 17 © CC Studio / Science Photo Library; p. 18 © iStockphoto.com / David T Gomez; p. 19 © Eddie Lawrence / Science Photo Library; p. 20 © 2008 Jupiterimages Corporation, © iStockphoto.com / Adrian Assalve; p. 23 © Mary Evans Picture Library; p. 24 © 2008 Jupiterimages Corporation, © 2008 Jupiterimages Corporation; p. 25 © iStockphoto.com / Paul Senyszyn; p. 26 © Andrew Parker / Alamy; p. 27 © 2008 Jupiterimages Corporation; p. 29 © iStockphoto.com / niknikon, © iStockphoto.com / Andreas Reh, © Imaging Australia. Image from BigStockPhoto.com; p. 35 © iStockphoto.com / AVTG; p. 38 © iStockphoto.com / dra_schwartz, © iStockphoto.com; p. 39 © Andrew Lambert Photography / Science Photo Library, © Laguna Design / Science Photo Library, © North Wind Picture Archives / Alamy; p. 40 © iStockphoto.com / Daniel Kourey, © iStockphoto.com / Eliza Snow; p. 41 © Bernhard Edmaier / Science Photo Library. Image from BigStockPhoto.com; p. 42 © Stephen Sweet. Image from BigStockPhoto.com; p. 43 © iStockphoto.com / Lisa Thornberg, © Horizon International Images Limited / Alamy; p. 44 © Jostein Hauge. Image from BigStockPhoto.com; p. 45 © Photofusion Picture Library / Alamy; p. 48 © iStockphoto.com / David Morgan; p. 55 © Leo Mason / Corbis; p. 57 © Sheila Terry / Science Photo Library; p. 58 © Cody Images / Science Photo Library; p. 59 © iStockphoto.com / Darryl Sleath, © Department for Transport; p. 60 © iStockphoto.com / Brian A Jackson, © iStockphoto.com / Ian Hamilton; p. 61 © iStockphoto.com / Eugene Kazimiarovich; p. 63 © iStockphoto.com / Mark Wragg, © Craige Bevil / Alamy; p. 68 courtesy of wikipedia.com / hajhouse; p. 69 © iStockphoto.com / Blackbeck; p. 71 © Art Wolfe / Science Photo Library; p. 73 © Dave Porter / Alamy; p. 74 © iStockphoto.com / Jason Reekie; p. 75 © iStockphoto.com / Michel de Nijs, © iStockphoto.com / Olaf Loose; p. 77 © iStockphoto.com / David Cannings-Bushell; p. 78 © United States Food & Drug Administration / Science Photo Library; p. 79 © Robert Brook / Science Photo Library; p. 80 © iStockphoto.com / Buretsu; p. 81 © 2008 Jupiterimages Corporation; p. 82 © iStockphoto.com / Robert Ellis

The publishers thank the Qualifications and Curriculum Authority for granting permission to reproduce questions from past National Curriculum Test papers for Key Stage 3 Science.

Name: ....

Organisms, Behaviour and Health	3-4	5-6	7-8
Cell, Tissues and Organs			
Using a microscope			
Studying plant cells			
Studying animal cells			
Designed for a purpose			
Cells, tissues and organs			
Organs and technology			
Reproduction			
Fertilisation and conception			
Courtship			
Becoming an adult			
What are twins?			
How a baby develops			
Birth of the baby			
Reproduction in flowering plants			

Chemical and Material Behaviour	3-4	5-6	7-8
Working in a laboratory			
Safety in the laboratory			
Hazard warning signs			
The Bunsen burner			
The best flame			
What makes things burn?			
Putting out a fire			
Fire precautions at school			
Acids and alkalis			
Indicators			
Weak and strong			
The pH meter			
Neutralisation			
Neutralisation in action			
Particles and Reactions			
Particle world			
Our watery world			
Spreading out			
How does heat change things?			
How does the mass change?			
Chemical reactions			
Fizzy reactions			
More about burning			
Everyday chemistry			
Reactions running backwards			

Student Progress Card

Name: ....

Energy, Electricity and Forces	3-4	5-6	7-8
Energy Transfers			
Types of energy			
Changing energy			
Tracking energy transfers			
What are fuels?			
Energy release from fuels			
Conductors and insulators			
Current in circuits			
Energy in circuits			
Forces and Speed			
Measuring the forces around you			
Different forces around you			
Balanced and unbalanced forces			
Speeding along			
Measuring the speed			
Friction			
Air resistance			
Streamlining and drag			

The Environment, Earth and Universe	3-4	5-6	7-8
Classification and Food Webs			
How do we classify?			
The five kingdoms			
Water for plants			
Why do we need plants?			
Are leaves bigger in the shade?			
What conditions do animals prefer?			
How plants and animals survive			
Food chains and webs			
Weathering and Fossils			
Looking at rocks			
Using rocks			
Weathering of rocks			
Pebble and powder science			
Rapid weathering			
Transporting rocks			
Rocks and heat			
Fossil past			
How fossil fuels are made			
Finding fossil fuels			

Topic 1 – Cells, Tissues and Organs

Using a microscope

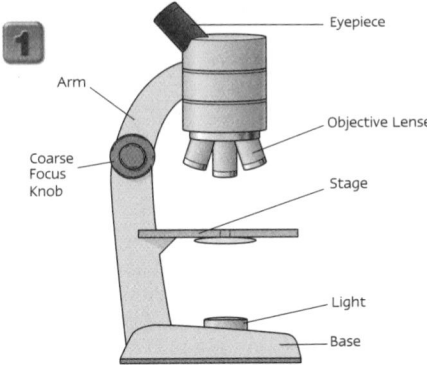

- Eyepiece
- Arm
- Objective Lenses
- Coarse Focus Knob
- Stage
- Light
- Base

Studying plant cells

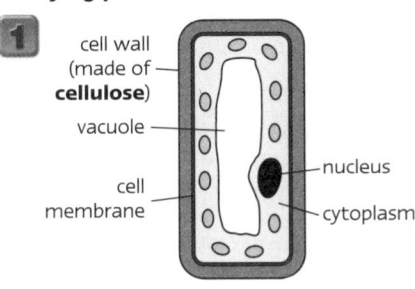

- cell wall (made of **cellulose**)
- vacuole
- cell membrane
- nucleus
- cytoplasm

Studying animal cells

Structure	Plant cell	Animal cell
nucleus	✔	✔
cell wall	✔	✗
cytoplasm	✔	✔
chloroplast	✔	✗
cell membrane	✔	✔
cell vacuole	✔	✗

Designed for a purpose

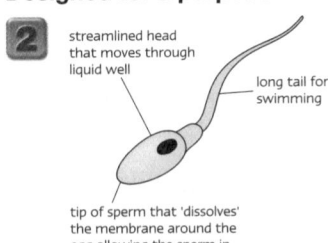

- streamlined head that moves through liquid well
- long tail for swimming
- tip of sperm that 'dissolves' the membrane around the egg allowing the sperm in

Cells, Tissues and Organs

Letter	Name	System
a	Lung	Respiratory
b	Heart	circulatory
c	Liver	digestive
d	Stomach	digestive
e	Small intestine	digestive

Organs and Technology

Brain → coordinates the body's activities

Lungs → get oxygen into the bloodstream

Heart → pumps blood around the body

Stomach → digests food

Kidneys → filter the blood

Topic 2 – Reproduction

Fertilisation and conception

a Sperm

b Fertilisation

c Ovary

d Egg

e Semen

f Conception

g External

h Testes

Courtship

Words required in this order:

strongest/offspring/fight or compete/dominant/harem/mated/same/species.

Becoming an adult

a On day one menstrual bleeding occurs.

b After two weeks an egg is released.

c After one week an egg is ripening and the uterus is building up.

d After three weeks the egg has almost reached the uterus.

What are twins?

One egg is fertilised by one sperm and that fertilised egg then splits into two. Each "half" develops into an identical organism.

The event described by the boy would not happen. One sperm could only fertilise one egg.

How a baby develops

Structure	Role
Uterus wall	Contains a very powerful muscle
Amniotic fluid	Protects the foetus
Umbilical cord	Attaches the foetus to the placenta
Placenta	Allows the transfer of materials between foetus and mother
Amnion	Retains fluid and helps to prevent infection

Birth of the baby

A human pregnancy is usually 38 weeks.

The head of the baby is usually pointing downwards.

During labour the uterus starts to contract.

When a baby is born we say it is delivered.

When a baby is ready to be born the mother goes into labour.

The passing out of amniotic fluid is known as the waters breaking.

Reproduction in flowering plants

Correct part – Pollination only occurs in plants.

Incorrect part – Fertilisation only occurs in animals.

Explanation – In plants pollen grains contain male sex cells that fertilise the female egg cell.

Topic 3 – Working in a laboratory

Safety in the laboratory

a Test tube pointing away from him; cork and pin to hold crispbread; test tube held in clamp; apparatus away from edge of bench; apparatus arranged over base of clamp for stability

b Place all the apparatus on a heat proof mat/ Use a temperature probe and a data logger rather than a thermometer that might break

Hazard Warning Signs

a Sarah has got both answers wrong.

b James has got both answers right – but he would lose one of the marks because for the corrosive description he has drawn two arrows one to a correct answer and one to a wrong answer – and if you do that you do not get the mark even if one of your suggestions is correct.

The Bunsen burner

a There is more air or oxygen

b Oxygen → carbon dioxide + water

The best flame

Activity	Flame required	Position of Air Hole	Reason for choice of flame
Lighting the Bunsen burner	Yellow	Fully closed	Easier to light and flame can be seen which is safer
Heating water in a beaker	Blue	Open	This is the hottest flame
Leaving the Bunsen burner alight whilst you prepare your next experiment	Yellow	Fully closed	So it is easy for everyone to see which makes it safer

    a Combustion

    b A blue flame shows that combustion is complete.

What makes things burn?

    a Oxygen, fuel, heat

    b The fire triangle

    c

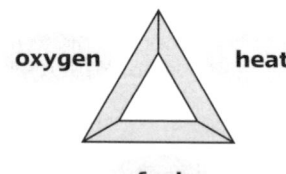

    d There is a limited amount of air and therefore oxygen in the bell jar so once this is used up the flame goes out. Oxygen is one of the three things needed for combustion.

    e The candle would burn for half the length of time.

    f To make the test fair you would need: Same size candle and the air tight seal between the container and the glass sheet it is standing on.

Putting out a fire

    a Carbon dioxide

    b It is heavier (or more dense) than air so it stops air containing the oxygen from reaching the fire – and without oxygen fire cannot continue to burn.

    c To force the water out of the cylinder.

    d Because it uses water and as water conducts electricity there is a danger of an electric shock

    e **i)** if you can safely tackle the fire yourself do so; **ii)** make sure everyone is out of the house;

    iii) close the door to prevent the fire from spreading;
    iv) call the fire brigade

Fire precautions at school

    a A carbonate and an acid.

    b acid + carbonate $\longrightarrow$ a salt + water+ carbon dioxide gas

    c Because otherwise the reaction would be going on all the time and the water and foam would be pushed out of the extinguisher.

    d Because of all the pupils and staff being in the school and the risk that they might be injured in the fire.

    e Because it might be a long time before anyone discovered it by which time it might have spread a long way from its original starting point.

Acids and alkalis

    a **i)** The substance which is most neutral is not normal soap – it is the one with the pH nearest to 7 which is normal facial wash or soap with moisturisers.

    ii) The most alkaline substance is normal soap as it has the highest pH and alkaline substances have high not low pH values. Normal skin with a pH of 5.5 is the most acidic substance listed here.

    b For the same reason the best description of Johnson's facial wash is that it is slightly acidic.

Indicators

    a Step 1 D, Step 2 G, Step 3 E, Step 4 B, Step 5 C, Step 6 A, Step 7 F.

    b B and D are the safety precautions.

Weak and strong

    a

Substance	Colour of Universal Indicator Solution	pH	Acid or Alkali
Water	Green	7	Neutral
Lemon juice	Orange	4	Acidic
Paint Stripper	Dark purple	13	Alkaline
Hair shampoo	Blue	8	Alkaline
Car battery acid	Red	1	Acidic
Vinegar	Orange	4	Acidic

The pH meter

    a pH meter

    b A pH meter is better for monitoring pH in situations where it changes over time and is not affected by colour of solution as Universal Indicator would be. Can be used for substances like soil without making a solution.

    c Buffer solution is a solution of known pH which is used to calibrate the meter.

    d A buffer solution has to have a known pH so distilled water, alcohol or sodium hydroxide are correct. The explanation needs to take into account the need for a repeatable reading and lack of any impurities in the solution that could contaminate the probe.

Neutralisation

    a **i)** Universal Indicator solution in the acid and **ii)** with a pH probe in the acid.

    b-c ◆ With 10 cc acid ■ With 20 cc acid

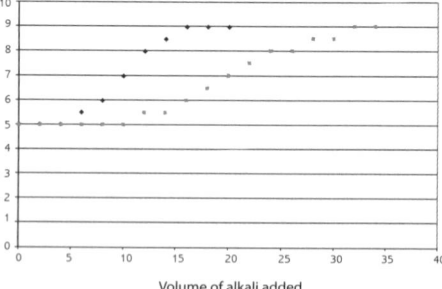

Change in pH with volume of alkali added

Neutralisation in action

    a Hydrochloric acid

    b Between 1 and 3 – a strong acid.

    c Around 8 or 9 – a weak alkali.

    b **i** Neutralisation reaction

    ii Looking at the equation the reaction of magnesium carbonate and hydrochloric acid gives off carbon dioxide which makes the mixture fizz.

    iii The test tube would feel warm.

Topic 4 – Particles and Reactions

Particle World

 a

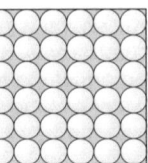 solid

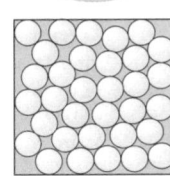 liquid

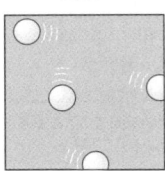 gas

b i) True; ii) False; iii) False; iv) True; v) True

Our watery world

2
a Volume of water; Initial start temperature

b They have not recorded the temperature of the two rooms.

c Label the axes clearly including the units;

use a scale that is even and uses as much of the paper as possible;

draw smooth curves;

give the graph a title that explains clearly what it is meant to show.

Spreading out

1 Diffusion; Evaporation; Because the particles of perfume would have the furthest to travel to reach the people at the back and so would take longer to get there which would mean they would be the last to smell the spilled perfume.

How does heat change things?

1 Chemical changes are usually irreversible.

i) and iii) are irreversible.

Boiling water to make steam – might happen whilst you were cooking a meal.

How does the mass change?

1 The water contained inside each crystal; to kill off mould; Silica crystals absorb water; salt; because rice will absorb water and keep the salt dry.

Chemical Reactions

2 Two of: heat changes, colour changes, fizzing.

Chemical reactions make new substances, physical changes of state do not OR physical changes of state can generally be easily reversed, chemical reactions cannot.

Neutralisation

Any sensible suggestion – indigestion tablets etc.

Fizzy reactions

1 Effervescence

There would be small bubbles of gas given off – the solution would fizz or effervesce.

Carbon dioxide

Combustion of fossil fuels, or respiration or any other sensible suggestion.

Oxygen

More about burning

2 Mass always increases

Because sometimes the gases are released into the air

Magnesium + Oxygen ➡ Magnesium oxide

Oxygen is about 20% of the air

Nitrogen makes up about 80% of the air

Nitrogen passes in and out of our lungs without being chemically altered in any way.

Everyday chemistry

2 Because some things only need to stick for a short time; a sticking plaster ; Soap and detergents are usually weak alkalis with a pH of 8 or 9; One end of the molecule sticks to the grease or dirt particle and the other end to a water molecule – this pulls the particle of dirt or grease away from our skin or clothes and into the water.

The water particles in hot water have more energy and are moving faster so will be better at separating the dirt from clothes. However those detergents that rely on a biological organism to remove the dirt work best at around 40 °C as this is body temperature and where all living things work best. Water that is too hot would destroy the biological element of these detergents.

Reactions running backwards

3 Chlorophyll and sunlight above and below the arrow; reactants are water and carbon dioxide and products are glucose and oxygen.

Photosynthesis and respiration in daylight and then respiration is continued when it is dark.

Topic 5 – Energy transfers

Types of energy

2 **a**

Type of energy	Example
Kinetic energy	Any moving object
Chemical energy	Food/ battery
Electrical energy	Any electrical appliance
Heat (or thermal energy)	Anything warm
Potential energy	A wound up clockwork mechanism
Gravitational energy	Anything at a height

b Nuclear energy is stored in the nucleus of an atom.

c Your energy is stored in food as chemical energy.

d Three sensible examples. 100g to make comparisons easier.

Changing energy

2
a She is standing still.

b i) 8; ii) Table shows there is no loss of energy as the total value is always the same.

Tracking energy transfers

2 **a, b** Answers are dependent on appliances chosen but must state that all energy transfers involve some loss of heat to the surroundings.

c When the Sankey diagrams are drawn the total amount of energy as shown in the width of the arrow must be the same at the start and at the end.

What are fuels?

1
a Coal; oil.

b Combustion

c Fuel + oxygen ➡ carbon dioxide +water (and heat)

Energy release from fuels

a ethanol (alcohol)

b Burning hydrogen only gives off water – no carbon monoxide, no sulphur dioxide produced.

c Hydrogen

d Oxygen

e Sugar cane will not run out as it takes a very short time to grow more unlike oil/petrol which would take many hundreds of years to produce more.

Conductors and insulators

a i-v

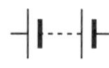

Battery

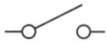

Open Switch   Closed Switch

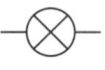

Lamp   Voltmeter

b

Item tested	Completed circuit	Did not complete circuit
A glass beaker		✔
An aluminium toy car	✔	
A wooden spoon		✔
A sheet of A4 paper		✔
A stainless steel fork	✔	

Make a circuit with a battery, some leads and a bulb. Have a gap in the circuit between two leads with crocodile clips on each one. Attach the crocodile clips to each item to be tested – if the current is flowing the bulb will light.

The stainless steel fork will let the current flow – the wooden spoon will not – this is because metals conduct electricity and non-metals (mostly) do not. This answer is partly right but the reason given is wrong.

Current in circuits

a E

b

switch 1	switch 2	bulb P	bulb Q	bulb R
open	open	off	off	off
open	closed	on	off	on
closed	open	off	off	off

Energy in circuits

a Voltage is the energy or 'push' that a battery (or other power supply) gives to a circuit. Current is how much electric charge is flowing in a circuit.

b Current; Parallel; Current

c 3.0 V

Topic 6 – Forces and Speed

Measuring the forces around you

a

Activity	Type of force
Moving a trolley around the supermarket	push
Shutting a door	push
Moving the pedals to ride a bicycle	push
In a tug of war	pull
Holding a strong dog on a lead	pull
Using a spanner to tighten a nut	turn
Turning on a tap	turn

b **i** More than 950N

ii Arrow drawn in direction that team B should be pulling the rope – away from Team A and the centre.

Different forces around you

a Liquids are denser and take up less space because the particles are closer together so are easier to transport.

b The fuel is being used up so the combined mass of the rocket and the fuel decrease as a result.

c **i** 27; 16.5

ii 10.5

iii The upward force is greater than the weight only after 10 seconds giving a net resultant upward force.

Balanced and unbalanced forces

a The car where the forward arrow is the longest is the one that is accelerating.

b The forward arrow is the longest

c It is not possible to tell where the force arrows are the same if a car is standing still or moving at a steady speed.

d The forces on the accelerating car are unbalanced which make it change speed – because the forward force is the greater the car will accelerate. Where forces are balanced an object will not change speed so if it is moving it will continue to move at a steady speed and if standing still will stay still so long as the forces are balanced.

Speeding along

a Does not change at all during the journey or the time for which speed is being measured.

b Average speed is the distance travelled in a particular time even though the speed at different parts of the journey will have been very different.

c

Time taken	Distance travelled	Average Speed
1 hour	25 kilometres	25km/h
10 seconds	100metres	10m/s
1 hour	15km	15 km/h
2 hours	50 kilometres	25km/h
3 hours	75 kilometres	25km/h

d 10m/s would be closest to the average speed of an Olympic sprinter.

Measuring the speed

a S I Units are standard units used by everyone all over the world.

b SI units mean that everyone can understand how much of something any one else is referring to.

c **i** Time – the second

ii Distance – the metre

d **i** Car milometer

ii Tape measure

iii 30cm ruler

iv Metre ruler

Friction

a The tyres on the road; The brake pads; Our hands on the steering wheel or feet on the pedals.

b If there is less friction between tyres and road the car is more likely to skid, more difficult to stop, danger of an accident etc.

c Snow chains increase friction between tyres and the snowy road – remove when the snow goes as too much friction would mean excessive wear on tyres.

Air resistance

 a **i–iii** The graph should show initial increase in speed which levels off until a steady speed is reached – then when parachute is opened speed reduces until a second steady speed is reached. The two points at which steady speeds are reached are the ones that should be marked. A parachute with a larger surface area would cause a greater reduction in speed and a slower terminal velocity.

b As a diver leaves the high board the force of gravity will act on her mass and cause her to accelerate as her weight will initially be greater than the air resistance – the rate of acceleration will slow down as the air resistance becomes greater because she is moving faster although in such a short space of time it is unlikely that terminal velocity will be reached. When she hits the water the drag will be much greater than the air resistance was and so her speed will slow very considerably.

Streamlining and drag

 a

It can make it easier to park a car in tight spaces	
It can increase the top speed	✗
It can make them easier to drive around sharp bends and corners	
It means a vehicle can travel further on the same amount of fuel	✗
It can make a car more stable	
It makes it easier to get a good paint finish	

b Many of the particles will move around the car if it has a streamlined shape rather than colliding with the car as it would if the shape were less streamlined.

c Greyhound, cheetah or any other animal known for being good at running!

Topic 7 – Classification and food webs

How do we classify?

Vertebrate group	One key feature
Fish	Gills/scaly skin
Birds	Eggs with brittle shells
Mammals	Suckle young/body hair
Amphibians	Moist skin
Reptiles	Tough leathery eggs

Rhinoceros beetle is an insect because it has 6 legs.

The five kingdoms

Organism	Possible evidence for	Possible evidence against
Fungi	Have cell walls or produce spores	No cellulose in cell wall or no chlorophyll
Bacteria	Have a cell wall	No chlorophyll, No cellulose in cell wall
Protists	Some can transfer light energy to chemical energy, some have cell walls	Organism able to move

Chlorophyll is a key feature of green plants, in fact it is what gives them their green colour. It allows the conversion of light energy into chemical energy in photosynthesis. Organisms lacking chlorophyll cannot carry out photosynthesis.

Water for plants

 Water sprayed onto hard tightly compacted soil will not easily penetrate to the roots and much will evaporate quickly in the hot climate. The rock filled trenches provide lots of gaps to allow water to penetrate right to the roots and the use of pipes reduces the risk of evaporation.

Water is essential for photosynthesis and growth and so an increased water supply will inevitably lead to increased yield.

Why do we need plants?

 a Waxy layer

b pore

c Palisade cells

Are leaves bigger in the shade?

 A more accurate answer would be: when it rains water soaks into the ground and is absorbed into the plant through its roots.

The waxy layer prevents excessive water loss by evaporation from the leaves.

Saying "to stop leaves soaking up water" is wrong because even without a waxy layer there are so few pores and they are so tiny that water could not enter a leaf anyway.

What conditions to animals prefer?

 a Similar numbers to previous column +/- 1.

b There is a pattern indicating woodlice prefer dark to light conditions.

c Suitable bar chart

d Protection from predators/prefer cooler damper conditions that are found in dark places.

How plants and animals survive

 Each penguin periodically gets a spell in the warmth of the huddle. But a large body of penguins presents a big clear target to a predator.

Food chains and webs

 Three link food chain
Leaf litter ➡ worm ➡ shrew ➡ owl
The producer is the leaf litter.

Topic 8 – Weathering and fossils

Looking at rocks

 Igneous links with crystalline, very hard and granite.

Sedimentary links with quite soft, formed in layers and limestone.

Metamorphic links with changed by heat and pressure from earlier rocks and marble.

Using rocks

a   88 years (as of 2008)

b   Good condition, clean, un-weathered.

c   Portland stone is easy to cut and carve and lasts for hundreds of years.

d   Too easily weathered, would not last, would not be able to read inscription after a few years.

Weathering of rocks

a   True
b   False
c   True
d   False
e   False
f   True

Pebble and powder science

 Correct words are in this order:

hard/wind/always/bumps/sharp/rounded/clue

Rapid weathering

a   slow
b   weather
c   more
d   easier
e   smooth, rounded
f   bigger, faster

Transporting rocks

Rock Type	Example	One property	One use	Easily weathered
Igneous	granite	hard, crystalline	road building	no
Sedimentary	limestone	soft, layers	buildings	yes
Metamorphic	marble	hard	statues	no

Rocks and heat

 Sandstone links with quartzite and heat.

Mudstone links with slate and pressure.

Limestone links with marble and heat.

Fossil past

 Words required in the following order:

preserved/rock/sedimentary/amber/tar/cliffs

How fossils are made

a   False
b   True
c   True
d   False
e   True
f   False
g   False
h   True

Finding fossil fuels

a   Bar chart with fuels on X axis and % on Y axis

b   Gas

c   North Sea oil production reduced, higher cost of imported oil, pollution concerns.

d   Nuclear

e   Nuclear is not a fossil fuel and that is the theme of this section.